PROPERTY OF
STAN
LEMESHOW

S0-AFA-689

SOLUTIONS MANUAL

APPLIED NONPARAMETRIC STATISTICS

Solutions Manual

APPLIED NONPARAMETRIC STATISTICS

Wayne W. Daniel
Georgia State University

HOUGHTON MIFFLIN COMPANY   BOSTON

Dallas   Geneva, Illinois
Hopewell, New Jersey   Palo Alto   London

Copyright © 1978 by Houghton Mifflin Company. All
rights reserved. Any or all of the items in this
manual may be adapted or reproduced in any way which
will make them more useful or convenient for college
teachers and their classes. Reproduction of these
items for commercial purposes is expressly prohibited.

Printed in the U.S.A.

ISBN: 0-395-25796-4

CONTENTS

CHAPTER 1   INTRODUCTION AND REVIEW

Chapter 1 does not contain exercises.

CHAPTER 2   PROCEDURES THAT UTILIZE DATA
FROM A SINGLE SAMPLE

2.1

Calculation of $X_i - M_0$ gives nine negative differences, two positive differences, and one zero difference.

$P(K \leq 2 | 11, 0.50) = 0.0328$

Since $0.0328 < 0.05$, reject H_0 and conclude that H_1 is true. k' = 2.   P value = 0.0328

2.2

Calculation of $X_i - M_0$ yields 3 negative differences and 12 positive differences. k = 3.

$P(K \leq 3 | 15, 0.50) = 0.0176$

Since $0.0176 < 0.05$, reject H_0.   k' = 3.
P value = 0.0176

2.3

$D_i = X_i - M_0$	Signed rank of $|D_i|$
+24.5	+6
+47.7	+9
+7.3	+3
+48.9	+10
-6.6	-2
+59.6	+14
+72.4	+15
+20.4	+5
+50.9	+11
+57.5	+12
-1.5	-1
+59.3	+13
+10.6	+4
+46.8	+8
+31.7	+7

$T_+ = 117$

$T_- = 3$ (Test statistic)

Since 3 < 16, reject H_0 at the 0.004 level of significance. P value < 0.004.

2.4

$D_i = X_i - M_0$	Signed rank of $|D_i|$
-12.32	-14
-26.32	-20
-5.32	-4
-10.32	-12
+5.68	+5.5
-4.32	-2.5
-18.32	-17
-22.32	-18
-6.32	-7
-24.32	-19
-4.32	-2.5
-14.32	-16
+0.68	+1
+5.68	+5.5
-11.32	-13
-8.32	-9
-9.32	-10
+9.68	+11
+6.68	+8
-13.32	-15

$$T_+ = 31 \text{ (Test statistic)}$$

$$T_- = 179$$

Since 31 < 38, H_0 can be rejected at the 0.005 level of

significance. P value < 0.005

2.5

$D_i = X_i - M_0$	Signed rank of $|D_i|$
+17	+6
-16	-5
-28	-14.5
+3	+2
-23	-11.5
+26	+13
+21	+10
+19	+8
+7	+4
+1	+1
-20	-9

(Continued)

3

$D_i = X_i - M_0$	Signed rank of $|D_i|$
+6	+3
-28	-14.5
+23	+11.5
0	--
+18	+7

$$T_+ = 65.5$$

$$T_- = 54.5 \text{ (Test statistic)}$$

Since $54.5 > 32$, H_0 cannot be rejected at a reasonable level of significance. P value > 0.107

2.6

Sample median = 38.4

The ordered sample: 8.1, 10.3, 10.5, 12.1, 18.3, 19.1, 27.8, 31.5, 35.5, 36.6, 40.1, 40.8, 40.9, 44.9, 45.2, 57.0, 59.1, 63.7, 63.9, 74.6

$M_L = 19.1$, $M_U = 45.2$

The confidence coefficient is 0.9586.

2.7

Sample median = 10

The ordered sample: 6, 6, 7, 7, 8, 8, 9, 10, 11, 12, 12, 13, 14, 15, 16

$M_L = 7$, $M_U = 13$

The confidence coefficient is 0.9648.

2.8

Sample median = 45.5

The ordered sample: 30, 30, 32, 34, 35, 40, 42, 45, 46, 50, 52, 55, 57, 57, 63, 64

$M_L = 35$, $M_U = 55$.

The confidence coefficient is 0.9234.

2.9

The ordered sample: 0.64, 0.65, 0.70, 0.71, 0.78, 0.82,

0.85, 0.86, 0.86, 1.00, 1.10

When n = 11 and 1 - α = 0.946, d = 12.

There are $\left[(11)(10)/2 \right]$ + 11 = 66 averages. The (66/2) +

1 = 34 smallest averages are as follows:

0.640	0.675	0.705	0.730	0.745	0.755	0.775
0.645	0.675	0.710	0.735	0.750	0.755	0.780
0.650	0.680	0.710	0.740	0.750	0.760	0.780
0.670	0.700	0.715	0.745	0.750	0.765	0.780

0.780	0.815
0.785	0.820
0.785	
0.800	

The 12 largest averages are as follows: 1.10, 1.05,

1.00, 0.98, 0.98, 0.975, 0.960, 0.940, 0.930, 0.930,

0.925, 0.910

The estimate of the population median is

   (0.815 + 0.820)/2 = 0.8175

The lower and upper limits of the 94.6% confidence
interval for the population median are 0.715 and 0.910.

2.10

The ordered sample (each value divided by 100):

13, 15, 140, 140, 190, 310, 430

When n = 7 and 1 - α = 0.969, d = 2.

There are a total of $\left[(7)(6)/2 \right]$ + 7 = 28 averages.
The 15 smallest averages (in original units) are:

```
1,300      7,750     14,000
1,400      7,750     14,000
1,500     10,150     16,150
7,650     10,250     16,250
7,650     14,000     16,500
```

The estimate of the population median is:

$(16,250 + 16,500)/2 = 16,375$

The two largest averages are: 43,000; 37,000.

The lower and upper limits of the 96.9% confidence interval for the population median are 1,400 and 37,000.

2.11

The ordered sample: 4290, 5280, 5280, 5555, 5610

With $n = 5$ and $1 - \alpha = 0.875$, $d = 2$.

There are $5(4)/2 + 5 = 15$ averages.

The eight smallest averages are: 4290, 4785, 4785,

4922.5, 4950, 5280, 5280, 5280

The point estimate of the population median is 5280.

The two largest averages are 5610.0 and 5582.5.

The lower and upper limits of the 87.5% confidence interval are 5582.5 and 4785.0.

2.12

$S = 11$, $s = 10$

Since $11 > 10$, reject H_0. P value $= 0.0593$

2.13

$S = 6$, $s = 6$

Since P value $= 0.0690$, H_0 cannot be rejected.

2.14

$S = 38$, $\quad s = 57(0.50) + 1.645 \sqrt{57(0.50)(0.50)} = 35$

Since $38 > 35$, reject H_0

2.15

$S = 4$, $\quad s = 5$ when $\alpha = 0.0065$

Since $4 < 5$, H_0 cannot be rejected. P value $= 0.0936$

2.16

$\hat{p} = 52/216 = 0.24$

$$0.24 \pm 1.96 \sqrt{\frac{(0.24)(0.76)}{216}}$$

0.24 ± 0.06

$C(0.18 \leq p \leq 0.30) = 0.95$

2.17

From Table A-4, the lower limit $= 0.236$, and the upper limit $= 0.675$.

2.18

From Table A-4, lower limit $= 0.238$, upper limit $= 0.664$.

2.19

n_1 = number of days with 50% or less = 10

n_2 = number of days with more than 50% = 20

$r = 14$

Critical values of r are 9 and 20

Since $9 < 14 < 20$, the hypothesis of randomness cannot be rejected.

2.20

n_1 = number of negative residuals = 8

n_2 = number of positive residuals = 7

$r = 7$

Critical values of r are 4 and 13

Since $4 < 7 < 13$, the hypothesis of randomness cannot be rejected.

2.21

n_1 = number of observations above 1435 = 17

n_2 = number of observations below 1435 = 15

$r = 20$

Critical values of r are 11 and 23

Since $11 < 20 < 23$, the hypothesis of randomness cannot be rejected.

2.22

n_1 = number of females = 11, n_2 = number of males = 5

$r = 6$

Critical values of r are 4 and 13

Since $4 < 6 < 13$, the hypothesis of randomness cannot be rejected.

2.23

$n' = 25$, $C = (25 + 1)/2 = 13$, $n = 12$

There are 9 plus signs and 3 minus signs.

$P(K \leq 3 | 12, 0.50) = 0.0729$

H_0 cannot be rejected.

2.24

$n' = 25$, $C = (25 +1)/2 = 13$, $n = 12$

There are 11 minus signs and 1 plus sign.

$P(K \leq 1 | 12, 0.50) = 0.0031$, reject H_0

2.25

The 15 differences, $X_i - 20$, are   2, 4, 17, 8, -5, -6,

2, -4, -2, -3, 3, -4, 0, -2, -5

$P(K \leq 6 | 14, 0.50) = 0.3954 = P$ value

The population median may be 20.

2.26

Sample median = 18

The ordered sample: 14, 15, 15, 16, 16, 17, 18, 18, 20,

22, 22, 23, 24, 28, 37

$M_L = 16$, $M_U = 23$

The confidence coefficient is 0.9648.

2.27

$P(r \geq 6 | 20, 0.25) = 0.3829 = P$ value

Cannot reject H_0: $p \leq 0.25$

2.28

$\hat{p} = 6/20 = 0.30$

From Table A-4, the lower limit = 0.140, upper limit = 0.533.

DATA FROM A SINGLE SOURCE

2.29

D_i = $X_i - 70$	Signed rank of $|D_i|$	D_i = $X_i - 70$	Signed rank of $|D_i|$
+10	+12	-14	-13
-2	-4	-24	-18
-40	-22	-22	-17
-3	-6	-31	-20
0	Delete	+2	+4
-8	-9.5	-34	-21
-1	-1.5	-1	-1.5
-5	-7.5	-30	-19
-17	-15.5	-9	-11
-41	-23	-16	-14
-5	-7.5	-17	-15.5
-2	-4	-45	-24
-8	-9.5		

$T_+ = 16$, P value < 0.005

2.30

The method based on the sign test is used.

Sample median = 61

The arrayed sample: 25, 29, 30, 36, 39, 40, 46, 48, 53, 53, 54, 56, 61, 62, 62, 65, 65, 67, 68, 68, 69, 69, 70, 72, 80

$M_L = 48$, $M_U = 67$

The confidence coefficient is 0.9566.

2.31

$r = 10$, $n_1 = 12$, $n_2 = 12$

Since 7 < 10 < 19, the null hypothesis of randomness cannot be rejected.

10

2.32

$S = 110$, $s = 200(0.50) + 1.645 \sqrt{200(0.50)(0.50)} = 112$

Since $110 < 112$, H_0 cannot be rejected.

2.33

$P(r \geq 11 \mid 25, 0.5) = 0.7878$. The data do not support ESP.

CHAPTER 3   PROCEDURES THAT UTILIZE DATA FROM TWO INDEPENDENT SAMPLES

3.1

$T = 7 + 3 = 10$, significant at 0.01 level

3.2

$T = 8 + 8 = 16$, significant at 0.001 level

3.3

$T = 3\ 1/2 + 6 = 9\ 1/2$, significant at 0.05 level

3.4

The sample median is 14.

Since 4 of the 116 observations are equal to the sample median, a method of handling ties must be employed. For demonstration purposes the first two methods mentioned in the text will be illustrated.

a. Eliminate from the analysis the 4 observations that are equal to the median. The resulting contingency table is as follows.

	Less than three months	Three months or more	Total
Above 14	33	23	56
Below 14	38	18	56
Total	71	41	112

$\hat{p} = (33 + 23)/(71 + 41) = 0.50$

$$T = \frac{(33/71) - (23/41)}{\sqrt{(0.50)(1 - 0.50)(1/71 + 1/41)}} = -0.98$$

Since $-1.96 < -0.98 < 1.96$, H_0 is not rejected.

P value $= 2(0.1635) = 0.3270$

b. Categorize the observations as exceeding the median or not exceeding the median. The resulting contingency table is as follows.

	Less than three months	Three months or more	Total
Above 14	33	23	56
14 or below	40	20	60
Total	73	43	116

$\hat{p} = (33 + 23)/116 = 0.48$

$$T = \frac{(33/73) - (23/43)}{\sqrt{(0.48)(1 - 0.48)(1/73 + 1/43)}} = -0.86$$

P value $= 2(0.1949) = 0.3898$

3.5

The sample median is $(34 + 57)/2 = 45.5$

Number	Sodium-deprived birds	Control birds	Total
Above sample median	12	4	16
Below sample median	5	11	16
Total	17	15	32

$\hat{p} = (12 + 4)/(16 + 16) = 0.50$

$$T = \frac{(12/17) - (4/15)}{\sqrt{(0.50)(1 - 0.50)(1/17 + 1/15)}} = 2.48$$

P value $= 2(0.0066) = 0.0132$

3.6

X	Rank	Y	Rank
		23	1
		40	2
42	3		
		45	4
		50	5
58	6		
62	7		
		68	8
73	9		
90	10		
Total	$\overline{35}$		

$w_\alpha = 5, \qquad w_{1-\alpha} = (5)(5) - 5 = 20$

H_0 cannot be rejected by the Mann-Whitney test.

P value $\leq 0.05, \qquad T = 35 - 5(6)/2 = 20$

3.7

X	Rank	Y	Rank	X	Rank	Y	Rank
		348	1	556	19.5		
428	2					569	21
436	3			572	22		
437	4			589	23		
440	5			605	24.5		
481	6			605	24.5		
		493	7	618	26		
500	9			652	27		
500	9			677	28		
500	9			680	29		
511	11					710	30
515	12			722	31		
526	13			724	32		
		530	14			766	33
538	15			778	34		
		546	16			780	35
547	17					819	36
552	18					876	37
		556	19.5				
				Total	$\overline{453.5}$		

$T = 453.5 - 26(27)/2 = 102.5$

$$z = \frac{102.5 - (26)(11)/2}{\sqrt{(26)(11)(26 + 11 + 1)/12}} = -1.35$$

Since $-1.35 < -1.645$, do not reject H_0.

P value $= 0.0885$

3.8

a. Graphic solution

$$w_{0.025} = 32, \qquad L \simeq -16, \qquad U \simeq 4$$

Graph for Exercise 3.8

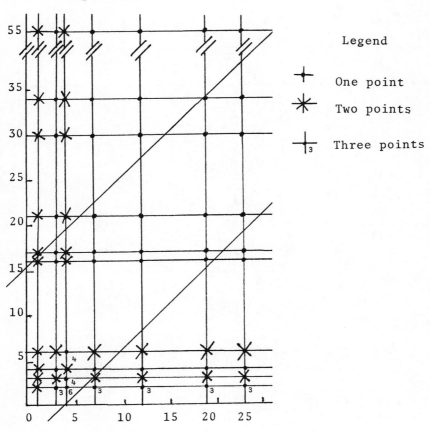

Since the horizontal and vertical scales are the
same, and since the constructed lines are each at a
45-degree angle to the horizontal axis, the magni-
tudes of the endpoints of the confidence interval,
except for sign, are determined once the constructed
lines cross either axis. The point where a line
crosses the vertical axis gives an endpoint value
of the confidence interval, but the sign is changed.
In the present example, the top line crosses the
vertical axis at approximately +16. The sign is
changed to give an endpoint of -16.

b. Arithmetic solution

Ordered samples are:

X: 1, 1, 3, 4, 4, 7, 12, 19, 23

Y: 2, 2, 2, 3, 3, 4, 6, 6, 16, 17, 21, 30, 34, 53

$w_{\alpha/2} = 32$

Y	1	1	3	4	4	7	12	19	23
2	-1	-1	1	2	2	5	10	17	21
2	-1	-1	1	2	2	5	10	17	21
2	-1	-1	1	2	2	5	10	17	21
3	-2	-2	0	1	1	4	9	16	20
3	-2	-2	0	1	1	4	9	16	20
4	-3	-3	-1	0	0	3	8	15	19
6	-5	-5	-3	-2	-2	1	6	13	17
6	-5	-5	-3	-2	-2	1	6	13	17
16	-15	-15	-13	-12	-12	-9	-4	3	7
17	-16	-16	-14	-13	-13	-10	-5	2	6
21	-20	-20	-18	-17	-17	-14	-9	-2	2
30	-29	-29	-27	-26	-26	-23	-18	-11	-7
34	-33	-33	-31	-30	-30	-27	-22	-15	-11
53	-52	-52	-50	-49	-49	-46	-41	-34	-30

L = -15,   U = 3

3.9

Observation	Group	Rank	$[r_i - (N + 1)/2]^2$
0	Y	1	
1.3	Y	2	
4.5	Y	3	
5.6	Y	4	

(Continued)

16

Observation	Group	Rank	$[r_i - (N + 1)/2]^2$
6.1	Y	5	
13.4	Y	6	
22.6	Y	7	
23.6	X	8	6.25
25.5	X	9	2.25
30.3	Y	10	
30.8	Y	11	
39.1	X	12	2.25
39.8	X	13	6.25
43.3	X	14	12.25
44.2	X	15	20.25
44.4	X	16	30.25
45.0	Y	17	
61.3	X	18	56.25
62.1	X	19	72.25
81.0	X	20	90.25
			M = $\overline{298.50}$

Since $198.50 < 298.50 < 464.50$, H_0 cannot be rejected.

P value > 0.10

3.10

Observation	Group	Rank	$[r_i - (N + 1)/2]^2$
328	X	1	20.25
336	Y	2	
347	X	3	6.25
372	Y	4	
425	Y	5	
428	Y	6	
433	X	7	2.25
434	Y	8	
478	X	9	12.25
607	X	10	20.25
			M = $\overline{61.25}$

Since $15.25 < 61.25 < 65.25$, H_0 cannot be rejected.

3.11

Answers vary, depending on results of randomization.

3.12

Answers vary, depending on results of randomization.

3.13

Ordered arrangement yielding r' = 9

36	43	50	53	55	56	56	56	56	57	58
Y	Y	Y	Y	X	Y	Y	Y	Y	Y	X

59	60	60	62	65	67	67	68	72	73
Y	Y	X	X	Y	X	X	X	Y	Y

Ordered arrangement yielding r" = 11

36	43	50	53	55	56	56	56	56	57	58
Y	Y	Y	Y	X	Y	Y	Y	Y	Y	X

59	60	60	62	65	67	67	68	72	73
Y	X	Y	X	Y	X	X	X	Y	Y

r = (9 + 11)/2 = 10

Since 10 > 5, H_0 cannot be rejected.

3.14

3	4	$\cdots$	12.2	12.8	15	17	40	$\cdots$	1100
X	X	$\cdots$	X	Y	X	X	Y	$\cdots$	Y

r = 4

$$z = \frac{4 - \left[\frac{2(16)(27)}{16 + 27} + 1 \right]}{\sqrt{\frac{2(16)(27)[2(16)(27) - 16 - 27)]}{(16 + 27)^2(16 + 27 - 1)}}} = \frac{-17.09}{3.02} = -5.66$$

Since -5.66 < -1.96, reject H_0 and conclude that the population distribution functions are different.

P value < 0.001

3.15

Observation	Group	Rank
54	Y	1
58	Y	2
67	Y	3
70	X	4
72	Y	5
73	X	6
74	Y	7
75	Y	8
76	X	9
79	X	10
81	X	11
80	X	12
82	X	13
83	X	14
84	Y	15
85	Y	16
86	X	17
96	Y	18
97	Y	19

$\bar{r} = 10.67$

$G = (4 - 10.67)^2 + (6 - 10.67)^2 + \cdots + (17 - 10.67)^2$

$= 128.00$

Since $128.00 < 148.9$, reject H_0 and conclude that there
is a difference in the responses.

$0.01 < P$ value < 0.05

3.16

Observation	Group	Rank
35	Y	1
38	Y	2
40	X	3
41	X	4
42	X	5
43	Y	6
48	X	7
50	X	8
51	X	9

(Continued)

19

Observation	Group	Rank
53	X	10
54	Y	11
55	Y	12
56	X	13
57	X	14
58	X	15
65	Y	16
69	Y	17
75	Y	18
85	Y	19
88	Y	20

$\bar{r} = 8.8$

$G = (3 - 8.8)^2 + (4 - 8.8)^2 + \cdots + (15 - 8.8)^2 = 159.60$

Since $159.60 < 196.4$, reject H_0.

3.17

$A = 6$, $\quad B = 6$, $\quad a = 6$, $\quad$ and critical $b = 2$

Since observed $b = 1 < 2$, reject H_0. H_0 may also be rejected at the 0.025 and 0.01 levels.

$0.001 < P$ value < 0.008

3.18

After rearranging the data, $A = 12$, $B = 10$, and $a = 9$.

From Table A-11, the critical value of b is found to be 3. Since the observed value of $b = 6$ (after re-arrangement) is greater than 3, H_0 cannot be rejected.

P value > 0.05

3.19

Answers vary, depending on results of randomization.

3.20

Observation	Group	Rank	$[r_i - (N + 1)/2]^2$
206	X	1	72.75
211	X	2	56.25
213	X	3	42.25
229	X	4	30.25
258	X	5	20.25
267	X	6	12.25
281	X	7	6.25
281	X	8	2.25
290	Y	9	
290	Y	10	
317	X	11	2.25
321	X	12	6.25
360	Y	13	
400	Y	14	
403	Y	15	
420	Y	16	
460	Y	17	
660	Y	18	
			251.00

$(N + 1)/2 = (18 + 1)/2 = 9.5$

Since $251 > 146$, P value > 0.10

3.21

Since the largest value in the two samples combined
(1.745) is an X value, and $T_1 = 1 + 3 = 4$, H_0 cannot
be rejected.

3.22

X	Rank	Y	Rank
18	1		
		21	2
		24	3
		28	4
124	5		
163	6		
	12		9

$T = 12 - 3(4)/2 = 6$

21

α	$w_{1-\alpha/2}$
0.001	(3)(3) - 0 = **9**
0.005	(3)(3) - 0 = 9
0.01	(3)(3) - 0 = 9
0.025	(3)(3) - 0 = 9
0.05	(3)(3) - 1 = 8
0.10	(3)(3) - 1 = 7

Since 6 < 7, P value > 0.20

3.23

X	Rank	Y	Rank
18	1		
		21	2
		24	3
		28	4
124	5		
163	6		

$S = 12$, $T = 12 - 3(4)/2 = 6$, P value > 0.20

3.24

X	Rank	Y	Rank
0.75	1		
1.76	2		
2.48	3		
4.88	4		
5.10	5		
		5.68	6
		5.68	7
6.01	8		
7.13	9		
		11.63	10
		16.30	11
		21.46	12
		33.30	13
		44.20	14
	32		73

DATA FROM TWO INDEPENDENT SAMPLES

$T = 32 - 7(8)/2 = 4$

Since $4 < 5$, reject H_0.

$0.002 < P$ value < 0.01

3.25

Median = 2.55

	Patients	Controls	Total
< Median	5	17	22
> Median	18	4	22
	23	21	44

$$\hat{p} = \frac{22}{44} = 0.50$$

$$T = \frac{(5/23) - (17/21)}{\sqrt{\dfrac{(0.50)(0.50)}{23} + \dfrac{(0.50)(0.50)}{21}}} = -3.92$$

P value < 0.001

3.26

$w_{\alpha/2} = 24$

			A		
B	32.0	32.5	34.0	40.0	49.0
27.0	5	5.5	7	13	22
28.0	4	4.5	6	12	21
30.0	2	2.5	4	10	19
30.5	1.5	2	3.5	9.5	18.5
31.0	1	1.5	3	9	18
31.0	1	1.5	3	9	18
31.5	0.5	1	2.5	8.5	17.5
32.5	-0.5	0	1.5	7.5	16.5
33.0	-1	-0.5	1	7	16
34.5	-2.5	-2	-0.5	5.5	14.5

A

B	51.5	52.0	52.0	65.0	74.0
27.0	24.5	25	25	38	47
28.0	23.5	24	24	37	46
30.0	21.5	22	22	35	44
30.5	21	21.5	21.5	34.5	43.5
31.0	20.5	21	21	34	43
31.0	20.5	21	21	34	43
31.5	20	20.5	20.5	33.5	42.5
32.5	19	19.5	19.5	32.5	41.5
33.0	18.5	19	19	32	41
34.5	17	17.5	17.5	30.5	39.5

$L = 4$, $U = 24$

3.27

$T = 4\ 1/2$,   P value > 0.05

3.28

	EH	EMR	Total
> 72	13	4	17
≤ 72	12	16	28
Total	25	20	45

$\hat{p} = (13 + 4)/(25 + 20) = 0.38$

$$T = \frac{(13/25) - (4/20)}{\sqrt{(0.38)(0.62)(1/25 + 1/20)}} = 2.20$$

Since $2.20 > 1.96$, H_0 is rejected.

P value < 0.002

3.29

$S = 96.5$, $T = 96.5 - 12(13)/2 = 18.5$

P value < 0.001

24

CHAPTER 4   PROCEDURES THAT UTILIZE DATA
            FROM TWO RELATED SAMPLES

4.1

The signs of the differences in observed values

$(X_i - Y_i)$ are -, +, +, +, +, +, +, +, +, +

P value = $P(K \leq 1|10, 0.50) = 0.0108$

4.2

The signs of the differences in observed values

$(X_i - Y_i)$ are +, +, +, +, +, +, +, +, +, 0, +, +, +

Eliminate the zero difference from analysis. Effective
n = 12.

P value = $P(K = 0|12, 0.50) = 0.0002$

4.3

The signs of the observed differences $(X_i - Y_i)$ are

+, +, +, +, +, +, +, +, +, +, +, +

P value = $P(K = 0|12, 0.50) = 0.0002$

4.4

$D_i = Y_i - X_i$	Signed Rank of $|D_i|$
0.72	+8
0.44	+6.5
0.26	+4
0.14	+2.5
0.14	+2.5
-1.10	-9
0.00	Omit
0.36	+5
-0.02	-1
0.44	+6.5

DATA FROM TWO RELATED SAMPLES

$T_+ = 35$, $T_- = 10$ (test statistic)

P value = 0.129

4.5

$D_i = Y_i - X_i$	Signed Rank of $|D_i|$
-53	-8
-13	-4
2	+1.5
-17	-5
-6	-3
-26	-7
-2	-1.5
-24	-6

$T_+ = 1.5$ (test statistic), $T_- = 34.5$

$0.008 <$ P value < 0.020

4.6

$D_i = Y_i - X_i$	Signed Rank of $|D_i|$
-0.32	-4
-0.49	-9
-0.41	-7
-0.64	-11
-0.26	-2
-0.33	-5
-0.18	-1
-0.48	-8
-0.39	-6
-0.53	-10
-0.28	-3

$T_+ = 0$ (test statistic), $T_- = 66$

P value < 0.010

4.7

Ordered D_i
-0.75
1.00
3.00

(Continued)

26

Ordered D_i

3.50
3.50 = M_L
5.75
6.25
7.25
7.75
8.75
9.25
10.50
11.00
12.25 = M_U
12.50
13.75
16.00
17.00

$K' = 4$, $C(3.50 \leq M \leq 12.25) = 0.969$

4.8

Ordered D_i = (After - Before)

12
34
35 = M_L
38
40
46
48
49
54 = M_U
58
83

$K' = 2$, $C(35 \leq M \leq 54) = 0.9344$

4.9

D_i = (After - Before)

+0.1
-0.2
+0.3
+0.3
-0.3
+1.1
+0.3
+0.6

(Continued)

27

D_i = (After - Before)

-0.5
+1.3
+0.5
+0.7
+1.4
+1.3
+0.6

d = 17

Ordered u_{ij}:   -0.50, -0.35, -0.30, -0.25, -0.20, -0.20, -0.10, -0.10, -0.10, -0.05, -0.01, 0.00, 0.00, 0.00, 0.05, 0.05, 0.05,* ···, 0.95,** 0.95, 1.00, 1.00, 1.00, 1.00, 1.05, 1.10, 1.20, 1.20, 1.25, 1.30, 1.30, 1.30, 1.35, 1.35, 1.40

*Lower limit,   **Upper limit

4.10

Ordered Values of D_i =   (Post - Pre)

-115
-20
-20
40
70
100
120
130
220
240
340
350
450
545
570
580
630
640
800
880

There are $[20(19)/2]$ + 20 = 210 values of u_{ij}. Since d = 38, only the 38 smallest and the 38 largest values have to be computed. They are as follows.

38 smallest values of u_{ij}

-115	25	70
-67.5	25	80
-67.5	40	85
-37.5	40	85
-22.5	40	95
-20	50	100
-20	50	100
-20	52.5	100
-7.5	55	100
2.5	55	100
7.5	55	110
10	62.5	110
10	70	

38 largest values of u_{ij}

880	665	580
840	640	575
800	635	575
760	630	570
755	625	570
730	615	562.5
725	610	560
720	610	557.5
715	605	550
712.5	605	545
690	600	545
685	592.5	540
672.5	587.5	

The approximate 99% lower and upper confidence limits are 110 and 540, respectively.

4.11

$$z = \frac{24 - 18}{\sqrt{24 + 18}} = 0.93$$

P value = 0.1762

4.12

$$z = \frac{9 - 5}{\sqrt{9 + 5}} = 1.07$$

P value = 2(0.1423) = 0.2846

4.13

The differences (X - Y) yield four negative, two positive, and one zero answers.

$P(K \leq 2|6, 0.5) = 0.3438 = $ P value.

4.14

Y_i = During, X_i = Before

$D_i = Y_i - X_i$	Signed Rank of $|D_i|$
+16.7	+5
+5.9	+1
+11.1	+4
+8.7	+3
+8.5	+2

$T_+ = 15$, $T_- = 0$ (test statistic)

P value = 0.031

Reject H_0, and conclude that high-dose PGE_1 infusion does increase shunt fractions.

4.15

The ordered differences (After - Before) are:

-32, -20, -5, 6, 7

$K' = 0$, $M_L = -32$, $M_U = 7$

Confidence coefficient = 1 - 2(0.0312) = 0.9376

4.16

The ordered values of D_i (Control - Experimental) are:

-1.1, -0.7, -0.2, 0.1, 0.1, 0.3, 1.4

There are $(7)(6)/2 + 7 = 28$ values of u_{ij}.

Since d = 2, only the two largest and the two smallest values have been computed. They are as follows.

Two smallest	Two largest
-1.1	1.4
-0.9	0.85

Therefore, we are 96.9% confident that the population median difference is between -0.9 and + 0.85.

4.17

The differences (Before - After) yield eight positive, and one negative, and one zero answers.

$P(K \le 1 | 9, 0.5) = 0.0196 = P$ value

4.18

X = Before,   Y = After

$D_i = Y_i - X_i$		Signed Rank of $\|D_i\|$	
+21	-2	+11	-1
+11	+12	+9	+10
-3	+27	-2.5	+13.5
+10	+4	+8	+4
-8	+6	-7	+6
+37	+5	+15	+5
+27	-3	+13.5	-2.5
+22		+12	

$T_+ = 107$, $T_- = 13$,   P value < 0.004

31

4.19

X = Before,   Y = After

$D_i = Y_i - X_i$		Signed Rank of $|D_i|$	
+5	+2	+12	+3.5
+5	0	+12	omit
+15	+8	+17.5	+15
+3	+4	+5.5	+8.5
+4	+4	+8.5	+8.5
+1	-1	+1.5	-1.5
+4	0	+8.5	omit
-5	-7	-12	-14
+3	+10	+5.5	+16
-2	+15	-3.5	+17.5

$T_+ = 140$, $T_- = 31$ (test statistic)

$0.005 <$ P value < 0.024, reject H_0

4.20

X = Before,   Y = After

$D_i = Y_i - X_i$		Signed Rank of $|D_i|$	
+28	+15	+14	+10
+10	+12	+7.5	+9
+10	+20	+7.5	+12.5
+3	+9	+2	+6
0	+8	omit	+4.5
+20	+5	+12.5	+3
+17	+8	+11	+4.5
-1		-1	

$T_+ = 104$, $T_- = 1$ (test statistic)

P value < 0.004, reject H_0

4.21

The differences (A - E) yield one zero, one positive, and ten negative differences.

$P(K \leq 1 | 11, 0.5) = 0.0059 =$ P value

DATA FROM TWO RELATED SAMPLES

<u>4.22</u>

$$z = \frac{67 - 10}{\sqrt{67 + 10}} = 6.50$$

P value < 0.0001

CHAPTER 5   CHI-SQUARE TESTS OF INDEPENDENCE
AND HOMOGENEITY

5.1

H_0: There is no association between hospital size and
willingness to return survey questionnaires

H_1: The two variables are related

X^2 = 56.8856,   df = 4

Expected Frequencies (E)*	$(O - E)^2/E$
152.338	12.9044
289.662	6.78669
84.4406	1.08222
160.559	0.569152
59.97	0.0687149
114.03	0.0361376
41.3586	15.897
78.6414	8.36047
6.89311	7.32731
13.1069	3.85354

*All expected frequencies are listed by column.

P value < 0.005

5.2

H_0: Opportunity levels and labor force mobility are
independent

H_1: The two variables are not independent

X^2 = 37.7885,   df = 1

Expected Frequencies (E)	$(O - E)^2/E$
28.8849	8.99066
22.115	11.7429
35.115	7.39553
26.8849	9.65949

P value < 0.005

5.3

H_0: There is no relationship between the two variables

H_1: There is a relationship between the two variables

X^2 = 12.3705,   df = 4

Expected Frequencies (E)	$(O - E)^2/E$
10.8308	4.30804
23.3846	0.243168
21.4154	2.02459
10.0923	2.38652
14.2769	0.36313
33.1692	1.40671
71.6154	0.0794026
65.5846	0.661086
30.9077	0.779268
43.7231	0.118574

0.01 < P value < 0.025

5.4

H_0: There is no relationship between fertility status and the presence of a psychiatric diagnosis

H_1: There is an association between the two variables

X^2 = 7.85256,   df = 1

Expected Frequencies (E)	$(O - E)^2/E$
24	2.04167
26	1.88461
24	2.04167
26	1.88461

$0.005 < P$ value < 0.01

5.5

H_0: The two variables are independent

H_1: The two variables are not independent

$X^2 = 29.5767,$ $df = 9$

Expected Frequencies (E)	$(O - E)^2/E$
6.92641	0.535782
7.61905	2.8003
10.8052	0.0600024
6.64935	8.12591
14.7186	0.939497
16.1905	0.00224088
22.961	0.402218
14.1299	0.0535834
15.368	0.364867
16.9048	6.02872
23.974	0.658746
14.7532	0.954831
12.987	4.94401
14.2857	1.95571
20.2597	0.149485
12.4675	1.60086

P value < 0.005

5.6

H_0: The two variables are not related

H_1: The two variables are related

X^2 = 11.5589,   df = 3

Expected Frequencies (E)	$(O - E)^2/E$
63.5742	2.05348
41.4258	3.15138
47.2266	0.0318561
30.7734	0.0488881
28.457	1.04646
18.543	1.60596
15.7422	1.42854
10.2578	2.19231

$0.005 < $ P value < 0.01

5.7

H_0: Residence in Youth and source of introduction to fishing among fishermen are independent

H_1: The two variables are not independent

X^2 = 15.3219,   df = 5

Expected Frequencies (E)	$(O - E)^2/E$
107.25	1.07751
36.4	0.531867
62.4	0.656409
44.2	0.00090495
29.9	0.562209
5.85	2.53376

(Continued)

Expected Frequencies (E)	$(O - E)^2/E$
57.75	2.00108
19.6	0.987759
33.6	1.21905
23.8	0.0016808
16.1	1.0441
3.15	4.70556

$0.005 < P$ value < 0.01

5.8

H_0: Legal treatment and social status are independent

H_1: The two variables are not independent

$x^2 = 29.851$, $df = 4$

Expected Frequencies (E)	$(O - E)^2/E$
9.38889	5.81492
7.46296	0.0386455
9.14815	5.13195
15.5278	1.32026
12.3426	1.75745
15.1296	0.00111065
14.0833	10.0833
11.1944	2.41032
13.7222	3.29307

P value < 0.005

5.9

H_0: Social class and political interests are not related

H_1: The two variables are related

38

CHI-SQUARE TESTS OF INDEPENDENCE AND HOMOGENEITY

$x^2 = 102.105$,   df = 4

Expected Frequencies (E)	$(O - E)^2/E$
211.183	14.2289
146.77	9.21189
34.0469	9.56597
123.908	2.04246
86.115	0.764716
19.9765	28.8903
123.908	12.2176
86.115	23.395
19.9765	1.78804

P value < 0.005

5.10

H_0: Value of shares owned and financial sophistication are not related

H_1: The two variables are related

Value of shares ($)	I	II	III
0-999	84	14	4
1,000- 4,999	141	25	4
5,000-19,999	137	47	12
20,000-99,999	98	49	14
over 1,000,000	52	37	38
	512	172	72

$x^2 = 109.326$,   df = 8

39

Expected Frequencies (E)	$(O - E)^2/E$
69.0794	3.22275
115.132	5.81192
132.741	0.136667
109.037	1.1172
86.0106	13.4486
23.2063	3.65231
38.6772	4.83662
44.5926	0.129968
36.6296	4.17766
28.8942	2.27397
9.71428	3.36134
16.1905	9.17871
18.6667	2.38095
15.3333	0.115942
12.0952	55.481

P value < 0.005

5.11

H_0: Sex and age when contact lenses first worn are independent

H_1: The two variables are not independent

$X^2 = 12.8131, \quad df = 2$

Expected Frequencies (E)	$(O - E)^2/E$
3.48315	0.631533
45.6292	1.27561
12.8876	6.443
6.51685	0.337544
85.3708	0.681792
24.1124	3.44367

P value < 0.005

5.12

H_0: The two groups are homogeneous with respect to extent of withdrawal

H_1: The two groups are not homogeneous

$X^2 = 12.3957$,   df = 1

Expected Frequencies (E)	$(O - E)^2/E$
5.53846	3.59402
6.46154	3.08058
6.46154	3.08058
7.53846	2.6405

P value < 0.005

5.13

H_0: The two groups do not differ with respect to rate of recovery

H_1: The two groups do differ with respect to rate of recovery

$X^2 = 5.1948$,   df = 1

Expected Frequencies (E)	$(O - E)^2/E$
14	1.14286
14	1.14286
11	1.45455
11	1.45455

0.01 < P value < 0.025

5.14

H_0: The two groups do not differ

H_1: The two groups do differ

X^2 = 3.9646,   df = 1

Expected Frequencies (E)	$(O - E)^2/E$
28.3011	0.78018
18.6989	1.18081
27.6989	0.797136
18.3011	1.20648

0.025 < P value < 0.05

5.15

H_0: The two groups do not differ

H_1: The two groups do differ

X^2 = 41.195,   df = 1

Expected Frequencies (E)	$(O - E)^2/E$
728.432	2.97707
122.568	17.6928
733.568	2.95619
123.432	17.5689

P value < 0.005

5.16

H_0: Marijuana users and nonusers differ with respect to alcohol use

H_1: The two groups do not differ

X^2 = 10.0608,   df = 1

Expected Frequencies (E)	$(O - E)^2/E$
61.41	0.343074
7.59	2.77577
27.59	0.763612
3.41	6.17833

P value < 0.005

5.17

H_0: The three groups are homogeneous

H_1: The three groups are not homogeneous

X^2 = 10.1083,   df = 6

Expected Frequencies (E)	$(O - E)^2/E$
24.8	0.0016131
14.7396	0.107774
28.0755	0.0411974
56.3849	0.00262748
46.8	2.97521
27.8151	0.833544
52.9811	0.167741
106.404	3.60901
140.4	0.958406
83.4453	0.151429
158.943	0.103534
319.211	1.15619

P value > 0.10

5.18

H_0: The three represented populations are homogeneous

H_1: The three represented populations are not homogeneous

$X^2 = 34.8599$,   df = 4

Expected Frequencies (E)	$(O - E)^2/E$
28.6667	0.655042
5.66667	5.66667
1.66667	1.06667
28.6667	3.25968
5.66667	18.8431
1.66667	0.266666
28.6667	0.992252
5.66667	3.84314
1.66667	0.266666

P value < 0.005

5.19

H_0: The two populations represented are homogeneous

H_1: The two populations are not homogeneous

$X^2 = 15.7942$,   df = 3

Expected Frequencies (E)	$(O - E)^2/E$
28	0
38	0
11.8788	5.22572
16.1212	3.85055

(Continued)

44

Expected Frequencies (E)	$(O - E)^2/E$
8.90909	1.87848
12.0909	1.38414
7.21212	1.98943
9.78788	1.4659

P value < 0.005

5.20

H_0: The adolescents from the three communities do not differ with respect to the variable of interest

H_1: The three populations do differ

$X^2 = 14.8994,$ df = 6

Expected Frequencies (E)	$(O - E)^2/E$
5.90164	0.746084
6.22951	0.797929
5.57377	2.29142
2.29508	5.9808
5.90164	0.13775
6.22951	0.0952978
5.57377	0.364947
2.29508	0.730795
6.19672	0.231113
6.54098	0.325445
5.85246	0.788033
2.40984	2.40983

0.01 < P value < 0.025

5.21

H_0: There is no difference in choice of major between the two groups

H_1: There is a difference

$X^2 = 0.811311,$ df = 4

Expected Frequencies (E)	$(O - E)^2/E$
22.1878	0.215726
24.8122	0.192912
37.2944	0.196283
41.7056	0.17552
8.96954	0.000103423
10.0305	0.0000924784
14.1624	0.00186307
15.8376	0.00166603
10.3858	0.0143302
11.6142	0.0128146

P value > 0.10

5.22

Homogeneity

5.23

Independence

5.24

Independence

5.25

Independence

CHI-SQUARE TESTS OF INDEPENDENCE AND HOMOGENEITY

<u>5.26</u>

Homogeneity

<u>5.27</u>

Homogeneity

CHAPTER 6   PROCEDURES THAT UTILIZE DATA FROM
THREE OR MORE INDEPENDENT SAMPLES

6.1

	Group			
	I	II	III	Total
> 168.05	4	5	2	11
≤ 168.05	8	0	3	11
	12	5	5	22

$X^2 = 6.53333,$ df = 2

Expected Frequencies (E)	$(O - E)^2/E$
6	0.666667
6	0.666667
2.5	2.5
2.5	2.5
2.5	0.1
2.5	0.1

$0.025 < P$ value < 0.05

6.2

	Population				
	I	II	III	IV	Total
> 30	0	7	4	7	18
≤ 30	9	3	5	2	19
	9	10	9	9	37

48

X^2 = 13.4717,   df = 3

Expected Frequencies (E)	$(O - E)^2/E$
4.37838	4.37838
4.62162	4.14794
4.86486	0.937087
5.13513	0.887766
4.37838	0.0326993
4.62162	0.0309784
4.37838	1.56974
4.62162	1.48712

P value < 0.005

6.3

	Controls	MD	Polio	Total
> 1.3	0	45	1	46
$\leq$ 1.3	16	16	19	51
	16	61	20	97

X^2 = 45.851,   df = 2

Expected Frequencies (E)	$(O - E)^2/E$
7.58763	7.58763
8.41237	6.84374
28.9278	8.92963
32.0722	8.05416
9.48454	7.58997
10.5155	6.84586

P value < 0.005

49

6.4

	Low	Normal	High	Total
> 0.75	9	19	7	35
≤ 0.75	11	20	10	41
	20	39	17	76

$x^2 = 0.283132$,   df = 2

Expected Frequencies (E)	$(O - E)^2/E$
9.21053	0.00481199
10.7895	0.00410783
17.9605	0.0601601
21.0395	0.0513547
7.82895	0.0877708
9.17105	0.0749264

P value > 0.10

6.5

	Normal	Moderate	Severe	Total
> 0.135	10	1	0	11
≤ 0.135	0	5	6	11
	10	6	6	22

$x^2 = 18.6667$,   df = 2

Expected Frequencies (E)	$(O - E)^2/E$
5	5
5	5

(Continued)

Expected Frequencies (E)	$(O - E)^2/E$
3	1.33333
3	1.33333
3	3
3	3

P value < 0.005

6.6

Ranks

Normal	Alcoholics With	Alcoholics Without
5	29.5	14.5
6	35	7.5
20.5	37	16.5
10.5	31	19
16.5	38	20.5
29.5	39	9
7.5	36	12
25	41	4
27	32	26
24	34	3
10.5	40	14.5
18		1
23		28
22		33
13		2

$R_1 = 258 \qquad R_2 = 392.5 \qquad R_3 = 210.5$

$$H = \frac{12}{41(41 + 1)} \left[\frac{258^2}{15} + \frac{392.5^2}{11} + \frac{210.5^2}{15} \right] - 3(41 + 1)$$

$$= 23.106$$

P value < 0.005

6.7

Ranks

Controls	LSD	UML
7.5	2	1
7.5	4.5	3
11	4.5	7.5
17.5	7.5	11
17.5	11	14
20.5	14	14
20.5	16	20.5
23.5	20.5	23.5
25		
26		
27		
$R_1 = 203.5$	$R_2 = 80.0$	$R_3 = 94.5$

$$H = \frac{12}{27(27 + 1)}\left[\frac{203.5^2}{11} + \frac{80^2}{8} + \frac{94.5^2}{8}\right] -3(27 + 1)$$

$$= 6.175$$

$0.025 < P \text{ value} < 0.05$

Correcting for ties:

$$\Sigma T = 3(2^3 - 2) + 2(3^3 - 3) + 2(4^3 - 4) = 186$$

$$H_C = \frac{6.175}{1 - (186/19656)} = 6.234$$

$0.025 < P \text{ value} < 0.05$

6.8

$$R_M = 361, \qquad R_F = 612, \qquad R_T = 353$$

$$H = \frac{12}{51(51 + 1)}\left[\frac{361^2}{17} + \frac{612^2}{17} + \frac{353^2}{17}\right] -3(51 + 1) = 11.547$$

$P \text{ value} < 0.005$

6.9

Ranks by Method

1	2	3	4	5	6
25	30	9	24	8	12
23	1	6	20	13	17
22	19	2	10	29	21
26	5	15	11	4	
32	31	27	16		
18			14		
3					
28					
7					

$R_1 = 184$ $R_2 = 86$ $R_3 = 59$ $R_4 = 95$ $R_5 = 54$ $R_6 = 50$

$$H = \frac{12}{32(32 + 1)} \left[\frac{184^2}{9} + \frac{86^2}{5} + \frac{59^2}{5} + \frac{95^2}{6} + \frac{54^2}{4} + \frac{50^2}{3} \right]$$

$-3(32 + 1) = 3.31$ (These intermediate calculations probably carried more decimals than those of the authors.)

P value > 0.10

6.10

$U_{12} = 11,$ $U_{13} = 39.5,$ $U_{23} = 37$

$J = 11 + 39.5 + 37 = 87.5,$ P value < 0.02311

6.11

$U_{6,7} = 23.5,$ $U_{6,8} = 52,$ $U_{7,8} = 42.5,$ $\Sigma n_i^2 = 216$

$J = 23.5 + 52 + 42.5 = 118,$ $N = 6 + 6 + 12 = 24$

$\Sigma n_i^2 (2n_i + 3) = 6^2 (2 \cdot 6 + 3) + 6^2 (2 \cdot 6 + 3) + 12^2 (2 \cdot 12 + 3)$

$= 4968$

$$z = \frac{118 - [(24^2 - 216)/4]}{\sqrt{\dfrac{24^2(2\cdot24 + 3) - 4968}{72}}} = 1.52$$

P value = 0.0643

6.12

$\overline{R}_1$ = 258/15 = 17.2, $\qquad$ $\overline{R}_2$ = 392.5/11 = 35.68

$\overline{R}_3$ = 210.5/15 = 14.03, $\qquad$ 0.15/3(2) = 0.025, $\qquad$ z = 1.96

$$1.96\sqrt{\frac{41(41 + 1)}{12}\left[\frac{1}{15} + \frac{1}{11}\right]} = 9.32$$

Since |17.2 - 35.68| = 18.48 > 9.32, conclude that the medians of population 1 and 2 are not equal.

Since |35.68 - 14.03| = 21.65 > 9.32, conclude that the medians of population 2 and 3 are not equal.

$$1.96\sqrt{\frac{41(41 + 1)}{12}\left[\frac{1}{15} + \frac{1}{15}\right]} = 8.57$$

Since |17.2 - 14.03| = 3.17 < 8.57, conclude that the medians of populations 1 and 3 may be equal.

6.13

$\overline{R}_1$ = 203.5/11 = 18.5, $\qquad$ $\overline{R}_2$ = 80/8 = 10

$\overline{R}_3$ = 94.5/8 = 11.81, $\qquad$ 0.20/(3)(3 - 1) = 0.033, z $\approx$1.84

$$1.84\sqrt{\frac{[27(27^2 - 1) - 186][1/11 + 1/8]}{12(26)}} = 6.75$$

Since $|18.5 - 10| = 8.5 > 6.75$, conclude that the medians of populations 1 and 2 are not equal.

Since $|18.5 - 11.81| = 6.69 < 6.75$, conclude that the medians of populations 1 and 3 may be equal.

$$1.84 \left[\frac{3[27(27^2 - 1) - 186}{6(27)(26)} \right]^{1/2} = 6.85$$

Since $|10 - 11.81| = 1.81 < 6.85$, conclude that the medians of populations 2 and 3 may be equal.

6.14

$\overline{R}_M = 361/17 = 21.24$, $\qquad \overline{R}_F = 612/17 = 36.00$

$\overline{R}_T = 353/17 = 20.76$, $\qquad 0.15/3(2) = 0.025$, $z = 1.96$

$$1.96 \sqrt{\frac{3(51 + 1)}{6}} = 9.99$$

Since $|21.24 - 36.00| = 14.76 > 9.99$, conclude that the medians of populations 1 and 2 are not equal.

Since $|21.24 - 20.76| = 0.48 < 9.99$, conclude that the medians of populations 1 and 3 may be equal.

Since $|36.00 - 20.76| = 15.24 > 9.99$, conclude that the medians of populations 2 and 3 are not equal.

6.15

Table of Ranks

Controls	Neonatal Hepatitis	Biliary Atresia
24	17	5
23	22	12
25	18	14.5
27	19	14.5

(Continued)

Controls	Neonatal Hepatitis	Biliary Atresia
26	20	2
	21	16
		3
		9
		8
		13
		1
		6
		10
		4
		11
		7
125	117	136

$$H = \frac{12}{27(28)} \left[\frac{125^2}{5} + \frac{117^2}{6} + \frac{136^2}{16} \right] - 3(28) = 20.17$$

Since $20.17 > \chi^2_2 = 10.597$, P value < 0.005

$\bar{R}_1 = 125/5 = 25$, $\qquad \bar{R}_2 = 117/6 = 19.5$

$\bar{R}_3 = 136/16 = 8.5$, $\qquad 0.15/3(2) \simeq 0.025$, $z = 1.96$

$$|25 - 19.5| < 1.96 \sqrt{\frac{27(28)}{12} \left[\frac{1}{5} + \frac{1}{6} \right]}$$

$|5.5 < 9.42$, not significant

$$|25 - 8.5| > 1.96 \sqrt{\frac{(27)(28)}{12} \left[\frac{1}{5} + \frac{1}{16} \right]}$$

$|16.5| > 7.97$, significant

$$|19.5 - 8.5| > 1.96 \sqrt{\frac{(27)(28)}{12} \left[\frac{1}{6} + \frac{1}{16} \right]}$$

$|11.0| > 7.45$, significant

6.16

Table of Ranks

I	II	III
13	7	16.5
18	3	10
9	1	11
14	2	15
12	5.5	16.5
	4	8
	5.5	
$R_I = \overline{66}$	$R_{II} = \overline{28}$	$R_{III} = \overline{77}$

$$H = \frac{12}{18(18+1)} \left[\frac{66^2}{5} + \frac{28^2}{7} + \frac{77^2}{6} \right] - 3(18+1) = 12.17$$

Since $12.17 > \chi_2^2 = 10.597$, P value < 0.005

$\overline{R}_1 = 66/5 = 13.20$, $\overline{R}_2 = 28/7 = 4.00$

$\overline{R}_3 = 77/6 = 12.83$, $0.20/3(2) = 0.033$, $z \simeq 1.84$

$$|13.20 - 4.00| > 1.84 \sqrt{\frac{18(19)}{12} \left[\frac{1}{5} + \frac{1}{7} \right]}$$

$|9.20| > 5.75$, significant

$$|13.20 - 12.83| < 1.84 \sqrt{\frac{18(19)}{12} \left[\frac{1}{5} + \frac{1}{6} \right]}$$

$|0.37| < 5.95$, not significant

$$|4.00 - 12.83| > 1.84 \sqrt{\frac{18(19)}{12} \left[\frac{1}{7} + \frac{1}{6} \right]}$$

$|-8.83| > 5.46$, significant

6.17

Table of Ranks

Carriers	HB-Antibody Positive	Controls
1	5	17
9	12	16
4	13	18
3	6	15
2	7	19
	11	14
	10	
	8	
$\overline{19}$	$\overline{72}$	$\overline{99}$

$$H = \frac{12}{19(20)} \left[\frac{19^2}{5} + \frac{72^2}{8} + \frac{99^2}{6} \right] - 3(20) = 14.327$$

Since $14.327 > \chi^2_2 = 10.597$, P value < 0.005

$\overline{R}_1 = 19/5 = 3.8,$ $\overline{R}_2 = 72/8 = 9.0$

$\overline{R}_3 = 99/6 = 16.5,$ $0.15/3(2) = 0.025,$ $z = 1.96$

$$|3.8 - 9.5| < 1.96 \sqrt{\frac{19(20)}{12} \left[\frac{1}{5} + \frac{1}{8} \right]}$$

$|-5.2| < 6.29$, not significant

$$|3.8 - 16.5| > 1.96 \sqrt{\frac{(19)(20)}{12} \left[\frac{1}{5} + \frac{1}{6} \right]}$$

$|-12.7| > 6.68$, significant

$$|9.0 - 16.5| > 1.96 \sqrt{\frac{19(20)}{12} \left[\frac{1}{8} - \frac{1}{6} \right]}$$

$|-7.5| > 5.96$, significant

6.18

$$U_{I,II} = 36, \qquad U_{I,III} = 48, \qquad U_{II,III} = 80$$

$$J = 36 + 48 + 80 = 164, \qquad N = 6 + 10 + 8 = 24$$

$$\sum_{i=1}^{k} n_i^2 = 6^2 + 10^2 + 8^2 = 200$$

$$\sum_{i=1}^{k} n_i^2 (2n_i + 3) = 6^2(2\cdot6 + 3) + 10^2(2\cdot10 + 3) + 8^2(2\cdot8+3)$$

$$= 4056$$

$$z = \frac{164 - [(24^2 - 200)/4]}{\sqrt{\dfrac{24^2(2\cdot24 + 3) - 4056}{72}}} = 3.73$$

On comparing our computed value of z = 3.73 with tabulated values in Table A-2, we find the probability of obtaining such a result due to chance alone, when H_0 is true, to be less than 0.001.

6.19

Table of Ranks

Nonsmokers	Light Smokers	Medium Smokers	Heavy Smokers
5.5	24	10.5	32.5
7	14	22.5	26
3.5	13	21	30
8	10.5	18.5	30
5.5	18.5	25	32.5
2	18.5	22.5	28
1	18.5	16	27
10.5	15		30
3.5			
10.5			
57	132	136	236

$$H = \frac{12}{33(34)} \left[\frac{57^2}{10} + \frac{132^2}{8} + \frac{136^2}{7} + \frac{236^2}{8} \right] - 3(34) = 27.489$$

Since $27.489 > \chi^2_3 = 12.838$, P value < 0.005

6.20

	Unwed Pregnant Girls	Married Pregnant Women	Unmarried Girls Not Pregnant	Total
> 60	11	22	15	48
≤ 60	14	24	22	60
	25	46	37	108

$X^2 = 0.443422$,   df = 2

Expected Frequencies (E)	$(O - E)^2/E$
11.1111	0.0011111
13.8889	0.000888897
20.4444	0.118358
25.5555	0.0946843
16.4444	0.126877
20.5555	0.101503

Since $0.443422 < 4.605$, P value > 0.10

6.21

	Very Isolated	Moderately Isolated	Rural Non-Isolated	Urban Ghetto	Total
> 33	2	10	15	18	45
≤ 33	21	13	8	5	47
	23	23	23	23	92

Expected frequencies are :

First row: $(23)(45)/92 = 11.25$

Second row: $(23)(47)/92 = 11.75$

$$X^2 = \frac{(2 - 11.25)^2}{11.25} + \dots + \frac{(5 - 11.75)^2}{11.75} = 25.533$$

Since $25.533 > X_3^2 = 12.838$, P value < 0.005

7.1

Table of Ranks

Patients	A	B	C
1	1.5	1.5	3
2	1	2	3
3	1	3	2
4	1	3	2
5	1	3	2
6	2.5	1	2.5
7	2	1	3
8	1	2	3
9	1.5	1.5	3
10	1	2	3
	$R_1 = \overline{13.5}$	$R_2 = \overline{20.0}$	$R_3 = \overline{26.5}$

$$\chi_r^2 = \frac{12}{10(3)(3 + 1)} (13.5^2 + 20.0^2 + 26.5^2)$$

$$- 3(10)(3 + 1) = 8.45$$

Since $7.378 < 8.45 < 9.210$, $0.01 < P$ value < 0.025

7.2

Table of Ranks

Dog	I	H	C
1	1	2	3
2	2	1	3
3	3	1	2
4	3	2	1
5	2	1	3

(Continued)

Dog	I	H	C
6	1	2	3
7	1	2	3
8	3	1	2
9	1	2	3
10	2	3	1
	$R_1 = 19$	$R_2 = 17$	$R_3 = 24$

$$\chi_r^2 = \frac{12}{10(3)(4)} (19^2 + 17^2 + 24^2) - 3(10)(3 + 1) = 2.60$$

P value > 0.10

7.3

Table of Ranks

Subject	0	24	72
1	1	2	3
2	1	2	3
3	1	2.5	2.5
4	1	3	2
5	1	2	3
6	1	3	2
7	1	2	3
8	1	2.5	2.5
	$R_1 = 8$	$R_2 = 19$	$R_3 = 21$

$$\chi_r^2 = \frac{12}{8(3)(3 + 1)} (8^2 + 19^2 + 21^2) - 3(8)(3 + 1) = 12.25$$

P value < 0.005

7.4

Table of Ranks

Serum	A	B	C	D
9	4	2.5	2.5	1
10	3	3	3	1
11	3	3	3	1
12	3.5	3.5	2	1
13	3	3	3	1
14	4	2	2	2
15	3	3	3	1
16	3.5	3.5	2	1
17	4	2	2	2
18	3	3	3	1
19	3	3	3	1
20	4	2.5	2.5	1
21	4	2	2	2
22	4	3	2	1
23	3.5	3.5	2	1
24	4	2.5	2.5	1
25	4	2.5	2.5	1
26	4	3	1.5	1.5
27	2.5	2.5	2.5	2.5
	$R_1 = 67$	$R_2 = 53$	$R_3 = 46$	$R_4 = 24$

$$\chi_r^2 = \frac{12}{19(4)(4+1)} (67^2 + 53^2 + 46^2 + 24^2) - 3(19)(4+1)$$

$$= 30.4737$$

P value < 0.005

7.5

Table of Ranks

Patient	C-1	C-2	Placebo	Test Drug
1	2	4	3	1
2	1.5	4	3	1.5
3	3	2	4	1
5	3	4	2	1
6	3	4	2	1

(Continued)

Table of Ranks

Patient	C-1	C-2	Placebo	Test Drug
7	3	4	2	1
9	4	3	2	1
10	4	3	1	2
12	2	4	3	1
13	3	4	2	1
14	4	3	2	1
15	4	1	3	2
18	1	2	3	4
19	4	2	3	1
22	4	2	3	1
	$R_1 = 45.5$	$R_2 = 46.0$	$R_3 = 38.0$	$R_4 = 20.5$

$$\chi_r^2 = \frac{12}{15(4)(4+1)} (45.5^2 + 46.0^2 + 38.0^2 + 20.5^2)$$

$$- 3(15)(4+1) = 17.02$$

P value < 0.005

7.6

$0.10/(3)(3 - 1) = 0.0167 \simeq 0.02$

$z = 2.05$, $\quad 2.05\sqrt{\dfrac{10(3)(3+1)}{6}} = 9.17$

$|19 - 17| = 2$, do not reject H_0

$|19 - 24| = 5$, do not reject H_0

$|17 - 24| = 7$, do not reject H_0

7.7

$0.05/(3)(3 - 1) = 0.0083 \simeq 0.01$

$z = 2.33$, $\quad 2.33\sqrt{\dfrac{8(3)(3+1)}{6}} = 9.32$

$|8 - 19| = 11$, reject H_0

$|8 - 21| = 13$, reject H_0

$|19 - 21| = 2$, do not reject H_0

7.8

$0.10/(4)(4 - 1) = 0.0083 \approx 0.01$

$z = 2.33,\qquad 2.33\sqrt{\dfrac{19(4)(4 + 1)}{6}} = 18.54$

$|67 - 53| = 14$, do not reject H_0

$|67 - 46| = 21$, reject H_0

$|67 - 24| = 43$, reject H_0

$|53 - 46| = 7$, do not reject H_0

$|53 - 24| = 29$, reject H_0

$|46 - 24| = 22$, reject H_0

7.9

Table of Ranks

Dog	Before	15	60	120
A	1	2	3	4
B	1	2	3.5	3.5
C	2	1	3	4
D	1	2	3	4
E	1	3	2	4
	$R_1 = 6$	$R_2 = 10$	$R_3 = 14.5$	$R_4 = 19.5$

$L = 6 + 2(10) + 3(14.5) + 4(19.5) = 147.5$

Since $147.5 > 145$, $p < 0.001$

66

7.10

A	B	C	D	E	F	G
8	20	22	32	42	46	54

$$L = 8 + 2(20) + 3(22) + 4(32) + 5(42) + 6(46) + 7(54)$$

$$= 1106$$

Since $994 < 1106$, P value < 0.001

7.11

Table of Ranks

Case	4	5	6	7	8	9	10
1	7	6	3	4.5	4.5	2	1
2	6	5	7	4	3	2	1
3	7	5.5	5.5	4	2	3	1
4	7	6	5	4	3	1.5	1.5
5	7	6	5	4	3	2	1
6	7	6	5	4	2	3	1
7	6	7	4	5	1	2	3
8	7	6	4	3	5	2	1
9	6	7	5	3	2	4	1
10	7	6	5	4	3	2	1
Rank sums:	67	60.5	48.5	39.5	28.5	23.5	12.5

$$L = 12.5 + 2(23.5) + 3(28.5) + 4(39.5) + 5(48.5)$$

$$+ 6(60.5) + 7(67) = 1377.5$$

Since $1377.5 > 1230$, P value < 0.001

7.12

Table of Ranks

Treatment	Block 1	2	3	4	Rank Sums
A	1.5	1	1		3.5
B	1.5	2		1	4.5
C	3		2	3	8
D		3	3	2	8

$$T = \frac{12(4 - 1)}{3(4)(3 - 1)(3 + 1)} \ (3.5^2 + 4.5^2 + 8^2 + 8^2)$$

$$\frac{3(3)(4 - 1)(3 + 1)}{(3 - 1)} = 6.1875$$

Since $6.1875 < \chi^2_3 = 6.251$, P value > 0.10

7.13

Ranks by Treatment

	0	1	2	4	9	18
	1	2	2	1	2	1
	1	1	2	1	2	2
	1	1	1	2	2	2
	1	1	2	2	2	1
	1	2	1	1	2	2
Rank Sums:	5	7	8	7	10	8

$$T = \frac{12(6 - 1)}{5(6)(2 - 1)(2 + 1)} \ (5^2 + 7^2 + 8^2 + 7^2 + 10^2 + 8^2)$$

$$- \frac{3(5)(6 - 1)(2 + 1)}{2 - 1} = 9$$

Since $9 < \chi^2_5 = 9.236$, P value > 0.10

7.14

Ranks by Treatment

	1	2	3	4	5
	2	1	1	2	1
	2	2	1	2	1
	1	1	1	2	2
	2	2	1	2	1
Rank Sums:	7	6	4	8	5

$$T = \frac{12(5 - 1)}{4(5)(2 - 1)(2 + 1)} (7^2 + 6^2 + 4^2 + 8^2 + 5^2)$$

$$- \frac{3(4)(5 - 1)(2 + 1)}{(2 - 1)} = 8$$

Since $7.779 < 8 < 9.488$, $0.05 < $ P value < 0.10

7.15

The C_j's are 6, 5, 1, 3.

The R_i's are 2, 3, 1, 3, 3, 3.

$$Q = \frac{4(4 - 1)(6^2 + 5^2 + 1^2 + 3^2) - (4 - 1)(15)^2}{4(15) - (2^2 + 3^2 + 1^2 + 3^2 + 3^2 + 3^2)} = 9.3158$$

Since $7.815 < 9.3158 < 9.348$, $0.025 < $ P value < 0.05

7.16

The C_j's are 2, 3, 9, 6, 6.

The R_i's are 1, 1, 4, 2, 1, 2, 3, 1, 1, 3, 2, 3, 2.

Two rows are deleted.

$$Q = \frac{5(4)(2^2 + 3^2 + 9^2 + 6^2 + 6^2) - (4)(26)^2}{5(26) - (1^2 + 1^2 + 4^2 + \cdots + 2^2)} = 9.3333$$

Since $7.779 < 9.3333 < 9.488$, $0.10 > P$ **value** > 0.05

7.17

The C_j's are 6, 8, 5, 3

The R_i's are 3, 3, 2, 2, 2, 3, 3, 1, 2, 1

$$Q = \frac{4(4 - 1)(6^2 + 8^2 + 5^2 + 3^2) - (4 - 1)(22)^2}{4(22) - (3^2 + 3^2 + 2^2 + \cdots + 1^2)} = 4.5882$$

Since $4.5882 < \chi_3^2 = 6.251$, P **value** > 0.10

7.18

$R_1 = 27.5,$ $R_2 = 53.5,$ $R_3 = 55,$ $R_4 = 44$

$$\chi_r^2 = \frac{12}{18(4)(4 + 1)}(27.5^2 + 53.5^2 + 55^2 + 44^2)$$

$$- 3(18)(4 + 1) = 15.983$$

Since $15.983 > 12.838$, P **value** < 0.005

7.19

$R_1 = 27.5,$ $R_2 = 53.5,$ $R_3 = 55,$ $R_4 = 44$

$0.18/(4)(3) = 0.015$, $z = 2.17$

$$2.17\sqrt{\frac{18(4)(5)}{6}} = 16.809$$

$|27.5 - 53.5| = 26$, significant

$|27.5 - 55| = 27.5$, significant

$|27.5 - 44| = 16.5$, not significant

$|53.5 - 55| = 1.5$, not significant

$|53.5 - 44| = 9.5$, not significant

$|55 - 44| = 11$, not significant

7.20

$R_1 = 38,$ $R_2 = 32,$ $R_3 = 20$

$$\chi_r^2 = \frac{12}{15(3)(3+1)} (38^2 + 32^2 + 20^2) - 3(15)(3+1)$$

$$= 11.2$$

Since $11.2 > 10.597$, P value < 0.005

7.21

$R_1 = 38,$ $R_2 = 32,$ $R_3 = 20$

$0.15/(3)(2) = 0.025$, $z = 1.96$

$$1.96\sqrt{\frac{15(3)(4)}{6}} = 10.735$$

$|38 - 32| = 6$, not significant

$|38 - 20| = 18$, significant

$|32 - 20| = 12$, significant

7.22

Ranks by Treatment

	A	B	C	D	E	F
	1	3	3	2	2	3
	1	2	2	3	1	3
	1	2	3	1	1.5	3
	1	3	1.5	1	1	3
	2	2	2	2	1	3
Rank Sums:	6	12	11.5	9	6.5	15

$$T = \frac{12(6-1)}{5(6)(3-1)(3+1)} (6^2 + 12^2 + \cdots + 15^2)$$

$$- \frac{3(5)(6-1)(3+1)}{(3-1)} = 15.125$$

Since $15.086 < 15.125 < 16.750$, $0.005 < $ P value < 0.01

7.23

Table of Ranks

	A	B	C	D
1	3		1	2
2		1	2	3
3	3	2	1	
4	3	2		1
	9	5	4	6

$$T = \frac{12(3)}{3(4)(2)(4)} (9^2 + 5^2 + 4^2 + 6^2) - \frac{3(3)(3)(4)}{2} = 5.25$$

Since $5.25 < \chi^2_3 = 6.251$, P value > 0.10

7.24

After eliminating the row of all 1's the

C_j's are 3, 3, 7, 6

R_i's are 2, 2, 3, 2, 2, 3, 2, 1, 2

$$Q = \frac{4(3)(3^2 + 3^2 + 7^2 + 6^2) - (3)(19^2)}{(4)(19) - (2^2 + 2^2 + 3^2 + 2^2 + 2^2 + 3^2 + 2^2 + 1^2 + 2^2)}$$

$$= 4.6364$$

Since $4.6364 < \chi^2_3 = 6.251$, P value > 0.10

7.25

After eliminating the row of all 1's, we have:

$C_1 = 4,$ $\quad C_2 = 8,$ $\quad C_3 = 7,$ $\quad C_4 = 4$

$R_1 = 3,$ $\quad R_2 = 2,$ $\quad R_3 = 2,$ $\quad R_4 = 2,$ $\quad R_5 = 3,$

$R_6 = 1,$ $\quad R_7 = 3,$ $\quad R_8 = 3,$ $\quad R_{10} = 2,$ $\quad R_{11} = 1,$

$R_{12} = 1,$ $\quad N = 23$

$$Q = \frac{4(3)(4^2 + 8^2 + 7^2 + 4^2) - 3(23)^2}{3(23) - (3^2 + 2^2 + \cdots + 1^2)} = 10.93$$

Since $9.348 < 10.93 < 11.345,$ $0.01 < P$ value < 0.025

8.1

CDQ

z_{L_i}	Expected Relative Frequency	Expected Frequency	$(O - E)^2/E$
2.30	0.0107	2.14	2.1400
2.06	0.0090	1.80	0.8000
1.70	0.0249	4.98	20.1607
1.33	0.0472	9.44	0.6307
0.97	0.0742	14.84	0.3144
0.61	0.1049	20.98	10.6959
0.25	0.1304	26.08	3.7733
-0.11	0.1425	28.50	1.0614
-0.47	0.1370	27.40	1.5898
-0.83	0.1159	23.18	2.2240
-1.19	0.0863	17.26	3.4709
-1.55	0.0564	11.28	3.4963
-1.91	0.0325	6.50	6.5000
	0.0281	5.62	5.6200
			62.4774

Since $62.4774 > \chi^2_{11} = 26.757$, P value < 0.005

BPS

z_{L_i}	Expected Relative Frequency	Expected Frequency	$(O - E)^2/E$
2.23	0.0129	2.58	2.5800
1.97	0.0115	2.30	0.2130
1.67	0.0231	4.62	0.0313
1.36	0.0394	7.88	0.4485
1.06	0.0577	11.54	6.2020
0.76	0.0790	15.80	1.1165

(Continued)

74

z_{L_i}	Expected Relative Frequency	BPS Expected Frequency	$(O - E)^2/E$
0.46	0.0992	19.84	0.1706
0.16	0.1136	22.72	1.7358
-0.14	0.1193	23.86	1.9723
-0.44	0.1143	22.86	3.4339
-0.74	0.1004	20.08	2.4963
-1.04	0.0804	16.08	1.0352
-1.35	0.0607	12.14	0.0609
-1.65	0.0390	7.80	63.1846
	0.0495	9.90	9.9000
			94.5809

Since $94.5809 > \chi_{12}^2 = 28.300$, P value < 0.005

8.2

$(O - E)^2/E$
0.0037
0.0058
0.0085
0.0338
0.0518

Since $0.0518 < \chi_3^2 = 0.0717$, p > 0.995

8.3

Expected frequency under H_0 is:

$$(7 + 12 + 6 + 10 + 12 + 6)/6 = 8.83$$

$$\chi^2 = \frac{(7 - 8.83)^2}{8.83} + \frac{(12 - 8.83)^2}{8.83} + \cdots + \frac{(6 - 8.83)^2}{8.83}$$

$$= 4.6243$$

Since $4.6243 < \chi_5^2 = 9.236$, P value > 0.10

75

8.4

Midpoint (x_i)	f_i	$x_i f_i$	$x_i^2 f_i$
850	9	7,650	6,502,500
950	23	21,850	20,757,500
1050	59	61,950	65,047,500
1150	42	48,300	55,545,000
1250	20	25,000	31,250,000
	153	164,750	179,102,500

$$\bar{x} = \frac{164,750}{153} = 1076.80$$

$$s^2 = \frac{153(179,102,500) - (164,750)^2}{(153)(152)} = 11,185.07$$

$$s = \sqrt{11,185.07} = 105.76$$

z_{L_i}	Expected Relative Frequency	Expected Frequency	$(O - E)^2/E$
	0.0044	0.67 ⎫ 7.26	0.4170
-2.62	0.0431	6.59 ⎭	
-1.67	0.1852	28.34	1.0062
-0.73	0.3544	54.22	0.4214
0.22	0.2899	44.35	0.1245
1.16	0.1056	16.16	0.9125
2.11	0.0174	2.66	2.6600
			5.5416

Since $5.5416 < \chi^2_3 = 6.251$, P value > 0.10

8.5

Expected Relative Frequency	Expected Frequency	$(O - E)^2/E$
0.0068	9.07	1.0391
0.0494	65.90	1.2020

(Continued)

Expected Relative Frequency	Expected Frequency	$(O - E)^2/E$
0.1543	205.84	0.0001
0.2676	356.98	0.0706
0.2786	371.65	0.1190
0.1740	232.12	2.4567
0.0604	80.57	1.6615
0.0090	12.01	0.0816
		6.6306

Since $6.6306 < \chi^2_7 = 12.017$, P value > 0.10

8.6

$$\widehat{\lambda} = \frac{0(18) + 1(18) + \cdots + 7(0)}{60} = \frac{79}{60} = 1.32$$

$f(0) = 0.2671, \qquad f(1) = 0.3526, \qquad f(2) = 0.2327$

$f(3) = 0.1024, \qquad f(4) = 0.0338, \qquad f(5) = 0.0089$

$f(6) = 0.0020, \qquad f(7) = 0.0004$

Expected Frequencies	$(O - E)^2/E$
16.026	0.2431
21.156	0.4708
13.962	0.0001
6.144	0.1193
$\left.\begin{array}{l} 2.028 \\ 0.534 \\ 0.120 \\ 0.024 \end{array}\right\}$ 2.706	0.0319
	0.8652

Since $0.8652 < \chi^2_3 = 6.251$, P value > 0.10

8.7

$$\hat{\lambda} = \frac{0(24) + 1(16) + \cdots + 12(1)}{120} = \frac{380}{120} = 3.17$$

$f(0) = 0.0420,$ $f(1) = 0.1332,$ $f(2) = 0.2110$

$f(3) = 0.2230,$ $f(4) = 0.1767,$ $f(5) = 0.1120$

$f(6) = 0.0592,$ $f(7) = 0.0268,$ $f(8) = 0.0106$

$f(9) = 0.0037,$ $f(10) = 0.0012,$ $f(11) = 0.0003$

$f(12) = 0.001$

Expected Frequencies	$(O - E)^2/E$
5.04	71.3257
15.98	0.0000
25.32	3.4306
26.76	2.8676
21.20	1.8132
13.44	1.4668
7.10	0.1704
3.22	0.9840
$\left.\begin{array}{l} 1.27 \\ 0.44 \\ 0.14 \\ 0.04 \\ 0.01 \end{array}\right\}$ 1.90	43.5842
	125.6425

Since $125.6425 > \chi_7^2 = 20.278$, P value < 0.005

8.8

$$\bar{x} = \frac{4(10) + 30(11) + \cdots + 1(19)}{324} = \frac{4237}{324} = 13.08$$

$$s^2 = \frac{324[4(10)^2 + 30(11)^2 + \cdots + 1(19)^2] - (4237)^2}{324(323)}$$

$$= 1.89805$$

$s = 1.38$, $D = 0.1937$

Since $0.1937 > \dfrac{1.63}{\sqrt{324}} = 0.0906$, P value < 0.01

Cumulative Frequency	$S(x_i)$	$z_i = (x_i - 13.08)/1.38$	$P(0 \leq Z \leq z_i)$
4	0.0123	-2.23	0.4871
34	0.1049	-1.51	0.4345
113	0.3488	-0.78	0.2823
217	0.6698	-0.06	0.0239
277	0.8549	0.67	0.2486
309	0.9537	1.39	0.4177
320	0.9877	2.12	0.4830
322	0.9938	2.84	0.4977
323	0.9969	3.57	0.5000*
324	1.0000	4.29	0.5000*

*Approximately

$F_0(x_i)$	$\lvert S(x_i) - F_0(x_i) \rvert$	$\lvert S(x_{i-1}) - F_0(x_i) \rvert$
0.0129	0.0006	0.0129
0.0655	0.0394	0.0532
0.2177	0.1311	0.1128
0.4716	0.1937	0.1273
0.7486	0.1063	0.0788
0.9177	0.0360	0.0628
0.9830	0.0047	0.0293
0.9977	0.0039	0.0100
1.0000*	0.0031	0.0062
1.0000*	0.0000	0.0031

*Approximately

8.9

$\bar{x} = 388.89$, $s = 55.95$, $D = 0.0826$

Since $0.0826 < 1.07/\sqrt{151} = 0.0871$, P value > 0.20

$S(x)$	$z = (x_i - 388.89)/55.95$	$F_0(x)$
0.0066	-3.38	0.0000*
0.0132	-2.57	0.0051
0.0265	-2.12	0.0170
0.0397	-1.86	0.0314
0.0927	-1.59	0.0559
0.1126	-1.41	0.0793
0.1457	-1.23	0.1093
0.1523	-1.14	0.1271
0.1722	-1.05	0.1469
0.1788	-0.96	0.1685
0.2119	-0.87	0.1922
0.2185	-0.78	0.2177
0.2583	-0.70	0.2420
0.2649	-0.61	0.2709
0.2980	-0.52	0.3015
0.3377	-0.43	0.3336
0.3642	-0.34	0.3669
0.3841	-0.25	0.4013
0.4371	-0.16	0.4364
0.4437	-0.07	0.4721
0.4901	0.02	0.5080
0.4967	0.11	0.5438
0.5563	0.20	0.5793
0.5762	0.29	0.6141
0.6556	0.38	0.6480
0.6622	0.43	0.6664
0.7218	0.56	0.7123
0.7881	0.73	0.7673
0.8146	0.82	0.7939
0.8411	0.91	0.8186
0.8477	1.00	0.8413
0.8874	1.09	0.8621
0.9272	1.27	0.8980
0.9338	1.36	0.9131
0.9404	1.45	0.9265
0.9603	1.63	0.9484
0.9801	1.72	0.9573
0.9934	1.81	0.9649
1.0000	1.99	0.9767

*Approximately

$|S(x_i) - F_0(x_i)|$	$|S(x_{i-1}) - F_0(x_i)|$
0.0066	0.0000
0.0081	0.0015
0.0095	0.0038
0.0083	0.0049
0.0368	0.0162
0.0333	0.0134
0.0364	0.0033
0.0252	0.0186
0.0253	0.0054
0.0103	0.0037
0.0197	0.0134
0.0008	0.0058
0.0163	0.0235
0.0060	0.0126
0.0035	0.0366
0.0041	0.0356
0.0027	0.0292
0.0172	0.0371
0.0007	0.0523
0.0284	0.0350
0.0179	0.0643
0.0471	0.0537
0.0230	0.0826
0.0379	0.0578
0.0076	0.0718
0.0042	0.0108
0.0095	0.0501
0.0208	0.0455
0.0207	0.0058
0.0225	0.0040
0.0064	0.0002
0.0253	0.0144
0.0292	0.0106
0.0207	0.0141
0.0139	0.0073
0.0119	0.0080
0.0228	0.0030
0.0285	0.0152
0.0233	0.0167

8.10

D = 0.0101

Since $0.0101 < 1.07/\sqrt{1334} = 0.0293$, P value > 0.20

$F_0(x)$	$S(x)$	$|S(x) - F_0(x)|$
0.0068	0.0045	0.0023
0.0562	0.0472	0.0090
0.2105	0.2016	0.0089
0.4781	0.4730	0.0051
0.7567	0.7466	0.0101
0.9307	0.9385	0.0078
0.9911	0.9903	0.0008
1.0000	1.0000	0.0000

8.11

$D = 0.0329$

Since $0.0329 < 1.07/\sqrt{60} = 0.1381$, P value > 0.20

$F_0(x)$	$S(x)$	$|S(x) - F_0(x)|$
0.2671	0.3000	0.0329
0.6197	0.6000	0.0197
0.8524	0.8333	0.0191
0.9548	0.9500	0.0048
0.9886	1.0000	0.0114
0.9975	1.0000	0.0025
0.9995	1.0000	0.0005
0.9999	1.0000	0.0001

8.12

Ordered Sample Values

X	Y	$S_1(x) - S_2(x)$
	9.3	$0 - 1/10 = -1/10$
10.2		$1/10 - 1/10 = 0$
	10.4	$1/10 - 2/10 = -1/10$
10.9		$2/10 - 2/10 = 0$
11.1		$3/10 - 2/10 = 1/10$
11.2	11.2 } Tie	$4/10 - 2/10 = 2/10$
		$4/10 - 3/10 = 1/10$
or		or
	11.2 } Tie	$3/10 - 3/10 = 0$
11.2		$4/10 - 3/10 = 1/10$

(Continued)

Ordered Sample Values

X	Y	$S_1(x) - S_2(x)$
11.3		5/10 - 3/10 = 2/10
11.3		6/10 - 3/10 = 3/10
11.4		7/10 - 3/10 = 4/10
	11.4⎫Tie	7/10 - 4/10 = 3/10
or		or
	11.4⎫Tie	6/10 - 4/10 = 2/10
11.4		7/10 - 4/10 = 3/10
	11.6	7/10 - 5/10 = 2/10
11.8		8/10 - 5/10 = 3/10
11.9		9/10 - 5/10 = 4/10
	11.9⎫Tie	9/10 - 6/10 = 3/10
or		or
	11.9⎫Tie	8/10 - 6/10 = 2/10
11.9		9/10 - 6/10 = 3/10
12.2		10/10 - 6/10 = 4/10
13.2		10/10 - 7/10 = 3/10
13.8		10/10 - 8/10 = 2/10
14.2		10/10 - 9/10 = 1/10
14.5		10/10 -10/10 = 0

$D = 4/10$, P value = 0.20

8.13

Ordered Sample Values

X	Y	$S_2(x) - S_1(x)$
	16	1/3 - 0 = 1/3
	18	2/3 - 0 = 2/3
	18	3/3 - 0 = 3/3
20		3/3 - 1/17 = 48/51
23		3/3 - 2/17 = 45/51
24		3/3 - 3/17 = 42/51
24		3/3 - 4/17 = 39/51
34		3/3 - 5/17 = 36/51
35		3/3 - 6/17 = 33/51
43		3/3 - 7/17 = 30/51
51		3/3 - 8/17 = 27/51
54		3/3 - 9/17 = 24/51
60		3/3 - 10/17 = 21/51
70		3/3 - 11/17 = 18/51
72		3/3 - 12/17 = 15/51

(Continued)

83

Ordered Sample Values

X	Y	$S_2(x) - S_1(x)$
72		3/3 - 13/17 = 12/51
107		3/3 - 14/17 = 9/51
223		3/3 - 15/17 = 6/51
358		3/3 - 16/17 = 3/51
437		3/3 - 17/17 = 0

$D^- = 3/3 = 1$

Since $1 > 1.52\sqrt{\dfrac{3 + 17}{3(17)}} = 0.95$, P value < 0.01

8.14

Ordered Sample Values

X	Y	$S_1(x) - S_2(x)$
118.5		1/9 - 0 = 1/9
135.0		2/9 - 0 = 2/9
	182.7	2/9 - 1/8 = 7/72
	204.0	2/9 - 2/8 = -2/72
261.7		3/9 - 2/8 = 6/72
	273.0	3/9 - 3/8 = -3/72
	297.7	3/9 - 4/8 = -12/72
	304.0	3/9 - 5/8 = -21/72
314.0		4/9 - 5/8 = -13/72
315.7		5/9 - 5/8 = -5/72
	324.3	5/9 - 6/8 = -14/72
336.9		6/9 - 6/8 = -6/72
	347.9	6/9 - 7/8 = -15/72
	351.2	6/9 - 8/8 = -24/72
352.7		7/9 - 8/8 = -16/72
565.5		8/9 - 8/8 = -8/72
797.5		9/9 - 8/8 = 0

$D = 24/72 = 0.33$

Since $0.33 < 4/9 = 0.44$, P value > 0.20

8.15

$S_1(x)$ - $S_2(x)$

```
   0   - 1/9 =   -1/9
   0   - 2/9 =   -2/9
   0   - 3/9 =   -3/9
   0   - 4/9 =   -4/9
   0   - 5/9 =   -5/9
 1/12  - 5/9 =  -17/36
 2/12  - 5/9 =  -14/36
 3/12  - 5/9 =  -11/36
 4/12  - 5/9 =   -8/36
 5/12  - 5/9 =   -5/36
 5/12  - 6/9 =   -9/36
 6/12  - 6/9 =   -6/36
 6/12  - 7/9 =  -10/36
 7/12  - 7/9 =   -7/36
 8/12  - 7/9 =   -4/36
 9/12  - 7/9 =   -1/36
10/12  - 7/9 =    2/36
10/12  - 8/9 =   -2/36
11/12  - 8/9 =    1/36
12/12  - 9/9 =   -3/36
12/12  - 9/9 =    0
```

$D = 5/9 = 0.56$,   P value = 0.05

8.16

$S_1(x)$	$S_2(x)$	$S_1(x)$ - $S_2(x)$
0.1064	0.0741	0.0323
0.2128	0.1605	0.0523
0.4043	0.2840	0.1203
0.5745	0.4444	0.1301
0.8298	0.5556	0.2742
0.9574	0.7037	0.2537
1.0000	0.7778	0.2222
1.0000	0.8642	0.1358
1.0000	0.9136	0.0864
1.0000	0.9506	0.0494
1.0000	1.0000	0.0000

$D = 0.2742$

85

Since $0.2742 > 1.36\sqrt{\dfrac{47 + 81}{(47)(81)}} = 0.2494$ and

$< 1.52\sqrt{(47 + 81)/(47)(81)} = 0.2787$

$0.05 > P$ value > 0.02

8.17

$$w_{1-\alpha} = \frac{1.36}{\sqrt{324}} = 0.0756$$

S(x)	S(x) - 0.0756	S(x) + 0.0756	L(x)	U(x)
0.0123	-0.0633	0.0879	0	0.0879
0.1049	0.0293	0.1805	0.0293	0.1805
0.3488	0.2732	0.4244	0.2732	0.4244
0.6698	0.5942	0.7454	0.5942	0.7454
0.8549	0.7793	0.9305	0.7793	0.9305
0.9537	0.8781	1.0293	0.8781	1
0.9877	0.9121	1.0633	0.9121	1
0.9938	0.9182	1.0694	0.9182	1
0.9969	0.9213	1.0725	0.9213	1
1.0000	0.9244	1.0756	0.9244	1

8.18

$$w_{1-\alpha} = \frac{1.22}{\sqrt{151}} = 0.0993$$

S(x)	S(x) - 0.0993	S(x) + 0.0993	L(x)	U(x)
0.0066	-0.0927	0.1059	0	0.1059
0.0132	-0.0861	0.1125	0	0.1125
0.0265	-0.0728	0.1258	0	0.1258
0.0397	-0.0596	0.1390	0	0.1390
0.0927	-0.0066	0.1920	0	0.1920
0.1126	0.0133	0.2119	0.0133	0.2119
0.1457	0.0464	0.2450	0.0464	0.2450

(Continued)

S(x)	S(x) - 0.993	S(x) + 0.0993	L(x)	U(x)
0.1523	0.0530	0.2516	0.0530	0.2516
0.1722	0.0729	0.2715	0.0729	0.2715
0.1788	0.0795	0.2781	0.0795	0.2781
0.2119	0.1126	0.3112	0.1126	0.3112
0.2185	0.1192	0.3178	0.1192	0.3178
0.2583	0.1590	0.3576	0.1590	0.3576
0.2649	0.1656	0.3642	0.1656	0.3642
0.2980	0.1987	0.3973	0.1987	0.3973
0.3377	0.2384	0.4370	0.2384	0.4370
0.3642	0.2649	0.4635	0.2649	0.4635
0.3841	0.2848	0.4834	0.2848	0.4834
0.4371	0.3378	0.5364	0.3378	0.5364
0.4437	0.3444	0.5430	0.3444	0.5430
0.4901	0.3908	0.5894	0.3908	0.5894
0.4967	0.3974	0.5960	0.3974	0.5960
0.5563	0.4570	0.6556	0.4570	0.6556
0.5762	0.4769	0.6755	0.4769	0.6755
0.6556	0.5563	0.7549	0.5563	0.7549
0.6622	0.5629	0.7615	0.5629	0.7615
0.7218	0.6225	0.8211	0.6225	0.8211
0.7881	0.6888	0.8874	0.6888	0.8874
0.8146	0.7153	0.9139	0.7153	0.9139
0.8411	0.7418	0.9404	0.7418	0.9404
0.8477	0.7484	0.9470	0.7484	0.9470
0.8874	0.7881	0.9867	0.7881	0.9867
0.9272	0.8279	1.0265		1
0.9338	0.8345	1.0331		1
0.9404	0.8411	1.0397		1
0.9603	0.8610	1.0596		1
0.9801	0.8808	1.0794		1
0.9934	0.8941	1.0927		1
1.0000	0.9007	1.0993		1

8.19

$$X^2 = \frac{(96 - 90)^2}{90} + \frac{(171 - 180)^2}{180} + \frac{(22 - 24)^2}{24} + \frac{(11 - 6)^2}{6}$$

$$= 5.183$$

Since $5.183 < \chi_3^2 = 6.251$, P value > 0.10

8.20

$\widehat{\mu} = 105,$ $\widehat{\sigma}^2 = 365.97,$ $\widehat{\sigma} = 19.13$

Score	z_{L_i}	Expected Relative Frequency	Expected Frequency	$(O - E)^2/E$
< 50		0.0020	0.60 ⎫ 2.82	0.2384
50- 59	-2.88	0.0074	2.22 ⎭	
60- 69	-2.35	0.0242	7.26	0.2187
70- 79	-1.83	0.0615	18.45	0.0164
80- 89	-1.31	0.1226	36.78	0.2819
90- 99	-0.78	0.1797	53.91	0.4472
100-109	-0.26	0.2052	61.56	0.0031
110-119	0.26	0.1797	53.91	0.2836
120-129	0.78	0.1226	35.78	0.7408
130-139	1.31	0.0615	18.45	0.3524
140-149	1.83	0.0242	7.26	0.0093
150-159	2.35	0.0074	2.22 ⎫ 2.94	0.3005
>159	2.88	0.0024	0.72 ⎭	------
				2.8923

Since $2.8923 < \chi^2_8 = 13.362$, P value > 0.10

8.21

$\widehat{\lambda} = (0)(10) + (1)(27) + \cdots + (9)(1) = 2.84$

$f(0) = 0.0584,$ $f(1) = 0.1659,$ $f(2) = 0.2356$

$f(3) = 0.2231,$ $f(4) = 0.1584,$ $f(5) = 0.0900$

$f(6) = 0.0426,$ $f(7) = 0.0173,$ $f(8) = 0.0061$

$f(9) = 0.0019$

Expected frequencies:

8.94	13.77
25.38	6.52
36.05	2.65
34.13	0.93 ⎫ 1.22
24.24	0.29 ⎭

$$\chi^2 = \frac{(10 - 8.94)^2}{8.94} + \frac{(27 - 25.38)^2}{25.38} + \cdots + \frac{(1 - 1.22)^2}{0.30}$$

$$= 4.0273$$

Since $4.0273 < \chi^2_7 = 12.017$, P value > 0.10

8.22

Expected

Relative Frequency	Expected Frequency		
$f(0)$ = 0.0010	0.10⎫		0.0059
$f(1)$ = 0.0098	0.98⎭ 1.08		
$f(2)$ = 0.0439	4.39		0.0848
$f(3)$ = 0.1172	11.72		1.9009
$f(4)$ = 0.2051	20.51		0.0117
$f(5)$ = 0.2461	24.61		0.2321
$f(6)$ = 0.2051	20.51		0.0127
$f(7)$ = 0.1172	11.72		0.0067
$f(8)$ = 0.0439	4.39		0.0346
$f(9)$ = 0.0098	0.98⎫		3.4133
$f(10)$= 0.0010	0.10⎭ 1.08		
			5.7027

Since $5.7027 < \chi^2_8 = 13.362$, P value > 0.10

8.23

Cumulative Frequency	$S(x)$	$z = (x - 80)/6$	$P(0 \le Z \le z)$
2	0.0556	-2.00	0.4772
4	0.1111	-1.33	0.4082
6	0.1667	-0.83	0.2967
8	0.2222	-0.67	0.2486
14	0.3889	-0.50	0.1915
17	0.4722	-0.33	0.1293
23	0.6389	0.00	0.0000
26	0.7222	0.17	0.0675
28	0.7778	0.67	0.2486
30	0.8333	1.00	0.3413
32	0.8889	1.17	0.3790
36	1.0000	2.00	0.4772

$F_0(x)$	$\lvert S(x_i) - F_0(x) \rvert$	$\lvert S(x_{i-1}) - F_0(x_i) \rvert$
0.0228	0.0328	0.0228
0.0918	0.0193	0.0362
0.2033	0.0366	0.0922
0.2514	0.0292	0.0847
0.3085	0.0804	0.0863
0.3707	0.1015	0.0182
0.5000	0.1389	0.0278
0.5675	0.1547	0.0714
0.7486	0.0292	0.0264
0.8413	0.0080	0.0635
0.8790	0.0099	0.0457
0.9772	0.0228	0.0883

$D = 0.1547$, P value > 0.20

8.24

$S_2(x) - S_1(x)$		
0.0933 - 0.0200 = 0.0733		
0.2867 - 0.0533 = 0.2334		
0.5533 - 0.1200 = 0.4333		
0.6733 - 0.2667 = 0.4066		
0.8133 - 0.3467 = 0.4666		
0.9667 - 0.5667 = 0.3000		
0.9067 - 0.7133 = 0.1934		
0.9400 - 0.8133 = 0.1267		
0.9733 - 0.9200 = 0.0533		
0.9867 - 0.9800 = 0.0067		
1.0000 - 1.0000 = 0.0000		

$D^- = 0.4666$

$$1.07\sqrt{\frac{150 + 150}{(150)(150)}} = (1.07)(0.11547005) = 0.1236$$

$1.22(0.11547005) = 0.1409$

$1.36(0.11547005) = 0.1570$

$1.52(0.11547005) = 0.1755$

$1.63(0.11547005) = 0.1882$

P value < 0.005

8.25

$$S_2(x) - S_1(x)$$

0.0300 - 0.0133	=	0.0167
0.0700 - 0.0333	=	0.0367
0.1200 - 0.0467	=	0.0733
0.2700 - 0.1133	=	0.1567
0.4700 - 0.2267	=	0.2433
0.6000 - 0.3933	=	0.2067
0.6800 - 0.5933	=	0.0867
0.7700 - 0.6933	=	0.0767
0.8200 - 0.8867	=	-0.0667
0.9800 - 0.9200	=	0.0600
1.0000 - 1.0000	=	0.0000

$D^- = 0.2433$

$$1.07\sqrt{\frac{150 + 100}{(150)(100)}} = (1.07)(0.129099) = 0.1381$$

$1.22(0.129099) = 0.1575$

$1.36(0.129099) = 0.1756$

$1.52(0.129099) = 0.1962$

$1.63(0.129099) = 0.2104$

P value < 0.005

CHAPTER 9   RANK CORRELATION AND OTHER
             MEASURES OF ASSOCIATION

9.1

Rank of

H	r	d_i^2
1	1	0
2	2	0
4	3	1
3	4	1
6	5	1
7	6	1
5	7	4
9	8	1
8	9	1
10	10	0
12	11	1
11	12	1
13	13	0
15	14	1
14	15	1
16	16	0
		14

$$r_S = 1 - \frac{6(14)}{16(16^2 - 1)} = 0.9794$$

Since $0.9794 > 0.7265$, P value < 0.002, for a two-sided
test.

9.2

Rank of

Intelligence	Social Dominance	d_i^2
6	5	1
3	1	4

(Continued)

92

Rank of Intelligence	Social Dominance	d_i^2
1	3	4
5	6	1
4	4	0
2	2	0
		10

$$r_S = 1 - \frac{6(10)}{6(6^2 - 1)} = 0.7143$$

Since $0.6000 < 0.7143 < 0.7714$, $0.1000 < $ P value $ < 0.2000$, for a two-sided test.

9.3

Rank of Serum mg	Bone mg	d_i^2
14	14	0
13	10	9
12	12	0
11	8	9
10	9	1
8.5	13	20.25
8.5	11	6.25
7	7	0
6	6	0
5	5	0
4	2	4
2	3	1
3	4	1
1	1	0
		51.5

$$r_S = 1 - \frac{6(51.5)}{14(14^2 - 1)} = 0.8868$$

Since $0.8868 > 0.7670$, P value < 0.002 for a two-sided test.

9.4

Rank of mean rate of return	Rank of Value	d_i^2	Rank of mean rate of return	Value	d_i^2
32	18	196	15.5	20	20.25
31	12	361	15.5	25	90.25
30	17	169	14	6	64
29	27	4	13	28	225
28	21	49	12	24	144
27	8	361	11	26	225
26	19	49	10	9	1
25	4	441	9	30	441
24	16	64	8	2	36
23	15	64	7	31	576
22	11	121	6	23	289
21	10	121	5	29	576
20	13	49	4	7	9
19	14	25	3	5	4
18	32	196	2	1	1
17	22	25	1	3	4
					5000.5

$$r_S = 1 - \frac{6(5000.5)}{32(32^2 - 1)} = 0.0835$$

$$z \simeq 0.0835\sqrt{32 - 1} = 0.46$$

P value = $2(0.5 - 0.1772) = 0.6456$

9.5

(X,Y) Rankings	Y pairs in natural order	Y pairs in reverse natural order
(1,12)	0	11
(2, 9)	2	8
(3, 1)	9	0
(4, 7)	3	5
(5, 3)	6	1
(6,10)	1	5
(7,11)	0	5
(8, 8)	0	4
(9, 2)	3	0

(Continued)

94

(X,Y) Rankings	Y pairs in natural order	Y pairs in reverse natural order
(10,6)	0	2
(11,4)	1	0
(12,5)	0	0
	P = 25	Q = 41

S = 25 - 41 = -16

$$\hat{\tau} = \frac{-16}{12(12-1)/2} = -0.24$$

Since -0.24 < -0.303, P value is greater than 0.20 for a two-sided test.

9.6

Y pairs in natural order	Y pairs in reverse natural order
13	1
13	1
13	1
18	0
3	8
12	0
12	0
12	0
3	5
3	5
7	2
3	4
3	4
1	6
6	0
4	1
2	2
1	3
2	1
1	1
1	0
0	0
P = 133	Q = 45

$$S = 88, \qquad T_y = \frac{8(7) + 7(6) + 3(2) + 2}{2} = 53$$

$$\hat{\tau} = \frac{88}{\sqrt{\frac{22(21)}{2}}\sqrt{\frac{22(21)}{2} - 53}} = 0.434$$

Since 0.434 > 0.394, P value < 0.01 for a two-sided test.

9.7

Y pairs in natural order	Y pairs in reverse natural order
11	0
11	0
11	0
11	0
9	2
10	0
7	2
6	0
6	0
3	3
3	2
2	2
2	0
2	0
1	0
0	0
P = 95	Q = 11

$$S = 84, \qquad T_x = \frac{5(4) + 3(2) + 2}{2} = 14, \qquad T_y = \frac{2(1)}{2} = 1$$

$$\hat{\tau} = \frac{84}{\sqrt{\frac{16(15)}{2} - 14}\sqrt{\frac{16(15)}{2} - 1}} = 0.7479$$

Since 0.7479 > 0.483, P value < 0.01, for a two-sided test.

9.8

Ordered values of X	Y	Y pairs in natural order	Y pairs in reverse natural order
2260	1830	5	0
2520	2100	4	0
3060	2290	3	0
3350	3290	1	1
3440	3130	1	0
3460	3400	0	0
		P = 14	Q = 1

$$S = 14 - 1 = 13, \qquad \hat{\tau} = \frac{13}{6(5)/2} = 0.867$$

Since $\hat{\tau} = 0.867$ = critical value of $\tau^* = 0.867$,

P value = 0.02 for a two-sided test.

9.9

Ordered values of Eye Track	Fixation Rate	Y pairs in natural order	Y pairs in reverse natural order
561.7	3.43	8	0
702.4	3.68	7	0
772.6	3.97	4	2
777.2	3.81	4	1
854.6	4.33	3	1
870.2	4.53	2	1
892.9	3.80	2	0
926.4	4.41	1	0
980.8	4.85	0	0
		P = 31	Q = 5

$$S = 31 - 5 = 26, \qquad \hat{\tau} = \frac{26}{9(8)/2} = 0.722$$

Since $\hat{\tau} = 0.722 = \tau^* = 0.722$, P value = 0.01 for a two-sided test.

9.10

Ordered values of total body water	Estimated lean body mass	Y pairs in natural order	Y pairs in reverse natural order
7.35	11.0	21	1
7.56	11.5	20	1
7.65	10.7	20	0
9.03	12.9	18	1
9.91	12.3	18	0
10.12	14.4	16	1
10.22	14.0	16	0
10.52	15.1	15	0
10.59	17.4	12	2
11.73	18.0	11	2
11.86	15.3	12	0
12.33	16.6	11	0
12.62	19.7	9	1
13.52	19.2	9	0
14.43	21.6	8	0
15.83	22.9	6	1
15.97	21.7	6	0
17.49	25.7	5	0
18.96	31.4	3	1
22.75	29.0	3	0
27.18	40.0	2	0
27.20	43.4	1	0
30.24	44.3	0	0
		P = 242	Q = 11

$S = 242 - 11 = 231$, $\qquad \hat{\tau} = \dfrac{231}{23(22)/2} = 0.9130$

$C_1 = 21 \qquad C_6 = 21 \qquad C_{11} = 20 \qquad C_{16} = 21 \qquad C_{21} = 22$

$C_2 = 21 \qquad C_7 = 21 \qquad C_{12} = 20 \qquad C_{17} = 21 \qquad C_{22} = 22$

$C_3 = 20 \qquad C_8 = 22 \qquad C_{13} = 21 \qquad C_{18} = 22 \qquad C_{23} = 22$

$C_4 = 21 \qquad C_9 = 20 \qquad C_{14} = 21 \qquad C_{19} = 21$

$C_5 = 21 \qquad C_{10} = 20 \qquad C_{15} = 22 \qquad C_{20} = 21$

$\Sigma C_i = 21 + 21 + \cdots + 22 = 484$

$\Sigma C_i^2 = 21^2 + 21^2 + \cdots + 22^2 = 10{,}196$

$\hat{\sigma}^2 = 4(10{,}196) - 2(484) - \dfrac{2[2(23) - 3][484]^2}{23(23 - 1)} = 1.7390$

$C\left[0.9130 - \dfrac{2\sqrt{1.7390}}{23(22)} (1.96) \leq \tau \leq 0.9130 + \right.$

$\left. \dfrac{2\sqrt{1.7390}}{23(22)} (1.96) \right] = 0.95$

$C(0.9028 \leq \hat{\tau} \leq 0.9232) = 0.95$

9.11

Ordered values of left eye	Right eye	Y pairs in natural order	Y pairs in reverse natural order
1.315	1.310	9	0
1.340	1.345	8	0
1.374	1.379	7	0
1.540	1.540	6	0
1.635	1.625	5	0
1.735	1.750	4	0
1.850	1.840	3	0
1.910	1.915	1	1
1.915	1.905	1	0
2.040	2.032	0	0
		$P = 44$	$Q = 1$

$S = 44 - 1 = 43, \qquad \hat{\tau} = \dfrac{43}{10(9)/2} = 0.9556$

$C_1 = 9 \qquad C_3 = 9 \qquad C_5 = 9 \qquad C_7 = 9 \qquad C_9 = 8$

$C_2 = 9 \qquad C_4 = 9 \qquad C_6 = 9 \qquad C_8 = 8 \qquad C_{10} = 9$

$$\Sigma C_i = 8(9) + 2(8) = 88, \qquad \Sigma C_i^2 = 8(81) + 2(64) = 776$$

$$\hat{\sigma}^2 = 4(776) - 2(88) - \frac{2(17)(88)^2}{10(9)} = 2.4889$$

$$C\left[0.9556 - \frac{2}{10(9)}(1.645)\sqrt{2.4889} \leq \hat{\tau} \leq 0.9556\right.$$

$$\left. + \frac{2}{10(9)}(1.645)\sqrt{2.4889}\right] = 0.90$$

$$C(0.9556 - 0.0577 \leq \hat{\tau} \leq 0.9556 + 0.0577) = 0.90$$

$$C(0.8979 \leq \hat{\tau} \leq 1.0000) = 0.90$$

9.12

Scatter Diagram

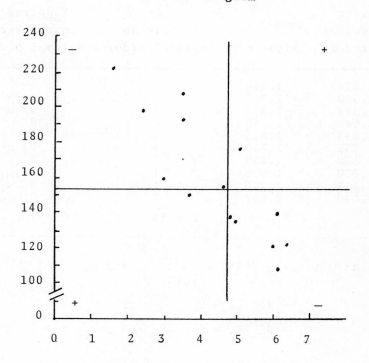

Median Y (Coronary blood flow) = 153

Median X (Hemoglobin) = 4.75

Counting down: -4,   Counting from right: -4

Counting up: -6,   Counting from left: -5

$S = |(-4) + (-4) + (-6) + (-5)| = 19$

P value = 0.0021

9.13

Median Y (Total DDT) = 1092.5

Median X (6 β-Hydroxycortisol) = 251

Counting from top: +2,   Counting from right: +5

Counting from bottom: +4,   Counting from left: +4

$S|2 + 5 + 4 + 4| = 15$, P value = 0.004963

See scatter diagram on following page.

Scatter Diagram for Exercise 9.13

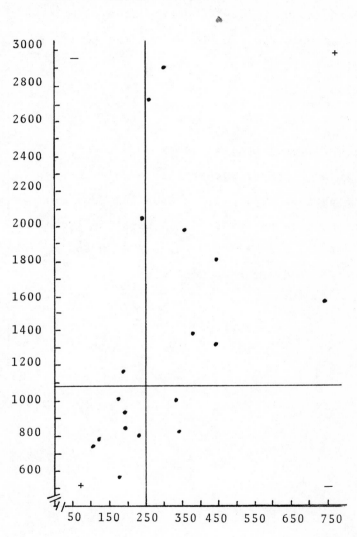

9.14

$$W = \frac{12(15^2 + 13^2 + 13^2 + 14^2 + 5^2) - 3(4)^2(5)(5 + 1)^2}{4^2(5)(5^2 - 1)}$$

$$= 0.40$$

$0.102 < P \text{ value} < 0.119$

9.15

$$W = \frac{\begin{array}{c} 12(12^2 + 10^2 + 8^2 + 28.5^2 + 24^2 + 25^2 + 35.5^2 + 22^2 \\ + 30^2 + 25^2) - 3(4)^2(10)(10 + 1)^2 \end{array}}{4^2(10)(10^2 - 1)}$$

$$= 0.568$$

$$X^2 = 4(10 - 1)(0.57) = 20.47$$

Since $20.47 > 16.919$, $P \text{ value} < 0.05$

9.16

$$W = \frac{\begin{array}{c} 12(5^2 + 7^2 + 12^2 + 19.5^2 + 24^2 + 20.5^2 + 30.5^2 \\ + 25.5^2 - 3(4)^2(8)(8 + 1)^2 \end{array}}{4^2(8)(8^2 - 1)}$$

$$= 0.8676$$

$P \text{ value} = 0.0000$

9.17

1970 pop.	No. of estab.	No. of funct.	No. of primary funct.	No. of funct. Units	R_j
37	26	26	27.5	23.5	140.0
36	28.5	28.5	27.5	28	148.5
35	22	17	16.5	21.5	112.0
34	30	30	29	30	153.0
33	14	19	19.5	12.5	98.0
32	37	37	37	35	178.0
31	35	32.5	32.5	36	167.0
30	33	32.5	31	33	159.5
29	36	34.5	35.5	37	172.0
28	4	1	1	5	39.0
27	31	34.5	32.5	32	157.0
26	12	9	13.5	11	71.5
25	32	31	34	31	153.0
24	20	10.5	12	19	85.5
23	24	25	25.5	25	122.5
22	13	12	15	14	76.0
21	18	18	19.5	16.5	93.0
20	17	14.5	16.5	15	83.0
19	34	36	35.5	34	158.5
18	27	27	30	27	129.0
17	21	22	21	21.5	102.5
16	28.5	28.5	25.5	29	127.5
15	19	23	23	20	100.0
14	11	14.5	10	12.5	62.0
13	2	7	5	6.5	33.5
12	25	21	22	23.5	103.5
11	6	2.5	3	4	26.5
10	8	13	10	10	51.0
9	23	24	24	26	106.0
8	10	8	7	9	42.0
7	16	20	18	18	79.0
6	9	10.5	10	8	43.5
5	1	5.5	3	1	15.5
4	3	4	6	2	19.0
3	15	16	13.5	16.5	64.0
2	7	5.5	8	6.5	29.0
1	5	2.5	3	3	14.5

$$W = \frac{12(140.0^2 + 148.5^2 + \cdots + 14.5^2) - 3(5)^2(37)(37 + 1)^2}{5^2(37)(37^2 - 1)} = 0.8591$$

$X^2 = 5(37 - 1)(0.8591) = 154.638$

Since $154.638 > 66.766$, P value < 0.005

9.18

$$W = \frac{12(24^2 + 14^2 + 10^2 + 16^2 + 21^2 + 20^2) - 3(5^2)(6)(6 + 1)^2}{(5)^2(6)(6^2 - 1)}$$

$= 0.3006$

$X^2 = 5(6 - 1)(0.3006) = 7.515$

P value > 0.10

9.19

d_i	d_i^2
4	16
4	16
2	4
-2	4
-2	4
1	1
4	16
-6	36
3	9
1	1
-2	4
2	4
-2	4
5	25
-2	4

$r_S = 1 - \dfrac{6(148)}{15(224)} = 0.7357$

$0.005 > $ P value > 0.001

9.20

$$\frac{d_i^2}{\begin{matrix}4\\4\\4\\1\\1\\9\\1\\4\\4\\4\end{matrix}}$$

$$r_S = 1 - \frac{6(36)}{10(99)} = 0.7818$$

P value = 0.005

36

9.21

$$W = \frac{12(5^2 + 16^2 + 16^2 + 9^2 + 14^2 + 24^2) - 3(16)(6)(49)}{16(6)(35)}$$

= 0.7643

P value < 0.001

9.22

Ordered values of academic Achievement	Self-Concept	Y pairs in natural order	Y pairs in reverse natural order
60	36	15	4
62	21	16	2
64	38	14	3
69	6	16	0
70	29	14	1
73	11	13	0
73	53	12	1
76	59	11	1
79	45	11	0
83	74	3	6
85	74	2	6
85	95	0	8

(Continued)

Ordered values of academic achievement	Self-concept	Y pairs in natural order	Y pairs in reverse natural order
87	66	3	3
88	89	0	5
89	69	1	4
93	61	3	1
97	65	1	1
97	66	1	1
98	89	0	1
99	60	0	0
		136	48

$$T_x = T_y = \frac{2(1) + 2(1) + 2(1)}{2} = 3$$

$$\hat{\tau} = \frac{136 - 48}{\sqrt{\frac{20(19)}{2} - 3}\sqrt{\frac{20(19)}{2} - 3}} = 0.471$$

Since $\hat{\tau} = 0.471 > \tau^* = 0.421$, P value < 0.005

9.23

Y pairs in natural order	Y pairs in reverse natural order
14	0
13	0
12	0
8	3
9	1
9	0
8	0
6	1
6	0
5	0
3	1
3	0
1	1
1	0
0	0

$P = 98, \qquad Q = 7, \qquad S = 98 - 7 = 92$

$\widehat{\tau} = \dfrac{92}{15(14)/2} = 0.876$

P value < 0.005

9.24

$$W = \dfrac{12(18^2 + 9^2 + 8^2 + 16^2 + 10^2 + 12^2 + 11) - 3(3)^2(7)(7 + 1)^2}{3^2(7)(7^2 - 1)}$$

$= 0.3254$

0.192 > P value > 0.112

9.25

d_i	d_i^2
0	0
-1	1
0	0
-1	1
-1	1
3	9
0	0
1	1
1	1
0	0

$r_S = 1 - \dfrac{6(14)}{10(99)} = 0.9152$

P value < 0.001

9.26

Y pairs in natural order	Y pairs in reverse natural order
16	1
15	1
15	0
10	4

(Continued)

108

Y pairs in natural order	Y pairs in reverse natural order
8	5
11	1
9	2
10	0
2	7
1	7
0	7
5	1
5	0
0	4
2	1
0	2
1	0
0	0
P = 110	Q = 43

$$\hat{\tau} = \frac{110 - 43}{18(17)/2} = 0.438$$

c_i	c_i^2
16	256
16	256
15	225
13	169
12	144
14	196
13	169
13	169
10	100
10	100
10	100
12	144
10	100
10	100
12	144
11	121
11	121
12	144
220	2758

$$\hat{\sigma}^2 = 4(2758) - 2(220) - \frac{2(2 \cdot 18 - 3)(220)^2}{18(17)} = 152.78$$

$$0.4379 \pm \frac{2}{18(17)} \sqrt{152.78} \ (1.96)$$

$$0.4379 \pm 0.1583$$

$$0.2796, \ 0.5962$$

9.27

C_i	C_i^2	C_i	C_i^2	
14	196	11	121	$\Sigma C_i = 196$
13	169	13	169	
13	169	12	144	
13	169	12	144	$\Sigma C_i^2 = 2572$
13	169	14	196	
14	196	14	196	
13	169	14	196	
13	169			

$$\hat{\sigma}^2 = 4(2572) - 2(196) - \frac{2(27)(196)^2}{15(14)} = 17.6000$$

$$0.8762 \pm \frac{2}{15(14)} \sqrt{17.6} \ (1.96)$$

$$0.8762 \pm 0.0783$$

$$0.7979, \ 0.9545$$

CHAPTER 10 SIMPLE LINEAR REGRESSION ANALYSIS

10.1

H_0: $\alpha = 5$, $\beta = -0.25$

H_1: $\alpha \neq 5$, $\beta \neq -0.25$

$Y = 5 - 0.25X$, $n_1 = 15$, $n_2 = 19$

$$X^2 = \frac{8}{50}\left[\left(15 - \frac{50}{4}\right)^2 + \left(19 - \frac{50}{4}\right)^2\right] = 7.76$$

Since $7.378 < 7.76 < 9.210$, $0.025 > P$ value > 0.01

H_0: $\beta = -0.25$, H_1: $\beta \neq -0.25$

$Y = 5.31 - 0.25X$, $n_1 = 12$

$$X_b^2 = \frac{16}{50}\left(12 - \frac{50}{4}\right)^2 = 0.08$$

Since $0.08 < 2.706$, P value > 0.10

$$Y_i - (-0.25X)$$

6.74	5.41	4.56	5.68
6.35	5.34	5.28	3.76
3.41	3.81	4.51	4.86
5.88	5.08	5.33	4.74
6.16	5.78	6.35	
5.80	4.62	6.99	
4.75	4.35	6.05	

Median $= (5.29 + 5.33)/2 = 5.31$

Scatter Diagrams for Exercise 10.1

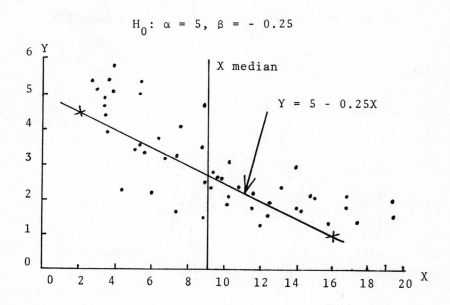

H_0: α = 5, β = - 0.25

X median

Y = 5 - 0.25X

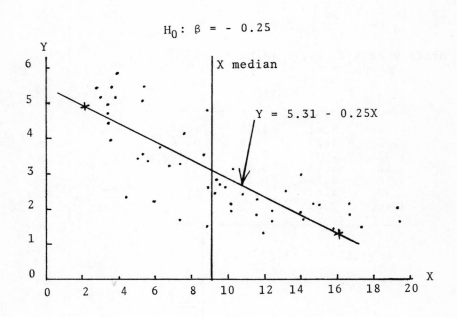

H_0: β = - 0.25

X median

Y = 5.31 - 0.25X

<u>10.2</u>

H_0: $\alpha = 4$, $\beta = 0.1$

H_1: $\alpha \neq 4$, $\beta \neq 0.1$

$n_1 = 6$, $n_2 = 5$

$$X^2 = \frac{8}{39}\left[\left(6 - \frac{39}{4}\right)^2 + \left(5 - \frac{39}{4}\right)^2\right] = 7.51$$

Since $7.378 < 7.51 < 9.210$, $0.025 > $ P value $ > 0.01$

H_0: $\beta = 0.1$, H_1: $\beta \neq 0.1$, $n_1 = 12$

$$X_b^2 = \frac{16}{39}\left(12 - \frac{39}{4}\right)^2 = 2.08$$

	$Y_i - 0.1X$	
6.6	2.80	0.60
4.0	3.10	2.69
4.9	1.64	3.35
4.0	2.85	2.80
5.3	2.50	1.00
4.06	1.18	5.53
3.95	3.30	0.10
3.80	2.70	3.40
2.40	1.65	0.65
4.45	3.50	7.40
5.55	1.08	8.58
3.60	3.35	5.40
5.50	1.55	13.40

The median of the deviations $Y_i - 0.1X$ is 3.35. The hypothesized line, then, is $Y = 3.35 - 0.1X$.

Scatter Diagram for Exercise 10.2

$H_0: \alpha = 4, \quad \beta = 0.1$

Median X

$Y = 4 + 0.10X$

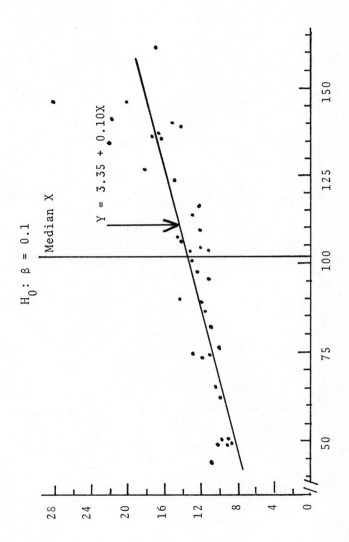

Scatter Diagram for Exercise 10.2

$H_0: \beta = 0.1$

Median X

$Y = 3.35 + 0.10X$

Scatter Diagram for Exercise 10.3

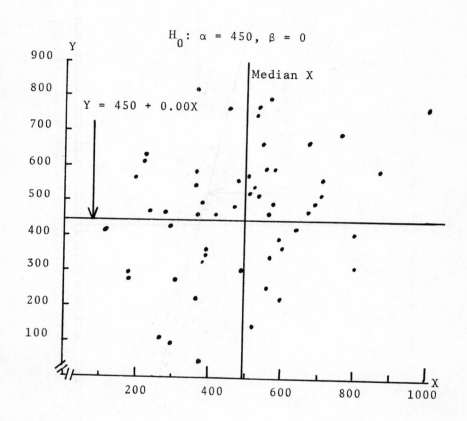

Scatter Diagram for Exercise 10.3

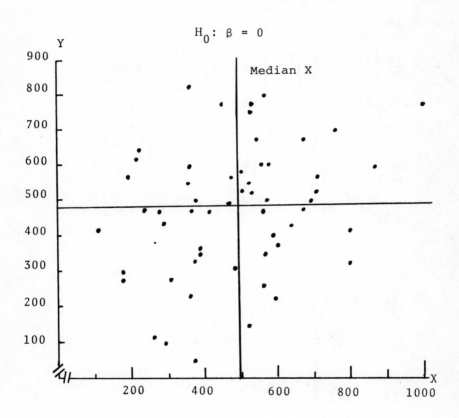

10.3

H_0: $\alpha = 450$, $\beta = 0$

H_1: $\alpha \neq 450$, $\beta \neq 0$

Median $X = 500$

$n_1 = 14$, $n_2 = 20$

$$X^2 = \frac{8}{56}\left[\left(14 - \frac{56}{4}\right)^2 + \left(20 - \frac{56}{4}\right)^2\right] = 5.14$$

Since $4.605 < 5.14 < 5.991$, $0.10 > P$ value > 0.05

H_0: $\beta = 0$, H_1: $\beta \neq 0$, $n_1 = 10$

$$X_b^2 = \frac{16}{56}\left(10 - \frac{56}{4}\right)^2 = 4.57$$

Since $3.841 < 4.57 < 5.024$, $0.025 < P$ value < 0.05

10.4

$$S_{12} = \frac{887.6 - 780.6}{705.0 - 660.0} = 2.3778$$

$$S_{13} = \frac{1039.2 - 780.6}{923.0 - 660.0} = 0.9833$$

$$S_{14} = \frac{1040.0 - 780.6}{923.0 - 660.0} = 0.9863$$

$$S_{15} = \frac{1122.8 - 780.6}{994.0 - 660.0} = 1.0246$$

$$S_{16} = \frac{1070.4 - 780.6}{1005.0 - 660.0} = 0.8400$$

$$S_{17} = \frac{1133.4 - 780.6}{1018.0 - 660.0} = 0.9855$$

$$S_{18} = \frac{1125.2 - 780.6}{1129.0 - 660.0} = 0.7348$$

$$S_{19} = \frac{1148.0 - 780.6}{1181.0 - 660.0} = 0.7052$$

$$S_{23} = \frac{1039.2 - 887.6}{923.0 - 705.0} = 0.6954$$

$$S_{24} = \frac{1040.0 - 887.6}{953.0 - 705.0} = 0.6145$$

$$S_{25} = \frac{1122.8 - 887.6}{994.0 - 705.0} = 0.8138$$

$$S_{26} = \frac{1070.4 - 887.6}{1005.0 - 705.0} = 0.6093$$

$$S_{27} = \frac{1133.4 - 887.6}{1018.0 - 705.0} = 0.7853$$

$$S_{28} = \frac{1125.2 - 887.6}{1129.0 - 705.0} = 0.5604$$

$$S_{29} = \frac{1148.0 - 887.6}{1181.0 - 705.0} = 0.5471$$

$$S_{34} = \frac{1040.0 - 1039.2}{953.0 - 923.0} = 0.0267$$

$$S_{35} = \frac{1122.8 - 1039.2}{994.0 - 923.0} = 1.1775$$

$$S_{36} = \frac{1070.4 - 1039.2}{1005.0 - 923.0} = 0.3805$$

$$S_{37} = \frac{1133.4 - 1039.2}{1018.0 - 923.0} = 0.9916$$

$$S_{38} = \frac{1125.2 - 1039.2}{1129.0 - 923.0} = 0.4175$$

$$S_{39} = \frac{1148.0 - 1039.2}{1181.0 - 923.0} = 0.4217$$

$$S_{45} = \frac{1122.8 - 1040.0}{994.0 - 953.0} = 2.0195$$

$$S_{46} = \frac{1070.4 - 1040.0}{1005.0 - 953.0} = 0.5846$$

$$S_{47} = \frac{1133.4 - 1040.0}{1018.0 - 953.0} = 1.4369$$

$$S_{48} = \frac{1125.2 - 1040.0}{1129.0 - 953.0} = 0.4841$$

$$S_{49} = \frac{1148.0 - 1040.0}{1181.0 - 953.0} = 0.4737$$

$$S_{56} = \frac{1070.4 - 1122.8}{1005.0 - 994.0} = -4.7636$$

$$S_{57} = \frac{1133.4 - 1122.8}{1018.0 - 994.0} = 0.4417$$

$$S_{58} = \frac{1125.2 - 1122.8}{1129.0 - 994.0} = 0.0178$$

$$S_{59} = \frac{1148.0 - 1122.8}{1181.0 - 994.0} = 0.1348$$

$$S_{67} = \frac{1133.4 - 1070.4}{1018.0 - 1005.0} = 4.8462$$

$$S_{68} = \frac{1125.2 - 1070.4}{1129.0 - 1005.0} = 0.4419$$

$$S_{69} = \frac{1148.0 - 1070.4}{1181.0 - 1005.0} = 0.4409$$

$$S_{78} = \frac{1125.2 - 1133.4}{1129.0 - 1018.0} = -0.0739$$

$$S_{79} = \frac{1148.0 - 1133.4}{1181.0 - 1018.0} = 0.0896$$

$$S_{89} = \frac{1148.0 - 1125.2}{1181.0 - 1129.0} = 0.4385$$

$$\text{Median} = \widehat{\beta} = \frac{0.5846 + 0.6093}{2} = 0.5970$$

10.5

The ordered array of S_{ij} values is as follows:

-4.7636	0.3805	0.4419	0.6093	0.8138	1.0246
-0.0739	0.4175	0.4737	0.6145	0.8400	1.1775
0.0178	0.4217	0.4841	0.6954	0.9833	1.4369
0.0267	0.4385	0.5471	0.7052	0.9855	2.0195
0.0896	0.4409	0.5604	0.7348	0.9863	2.3778
0.1348	0.4417	0.5846	0.7853	0.9916	4.8462

$$S_{\alpha/2} = 20, \qquad C_{\alpha/2} = 20 - 2 = 18, \qquad k = \frac{36 - 18}{2} = 9$$

$$\widehat{\beta}_L = 0.4217, \qquad \widehat{\beta}_U = 0.9855$$

10.6

$$S_{12} = \frac{9.5 - 8.7}{18.0 - 9.5} = 0.0941$$

$$S_{13} = \frac{15.4 - 8.7}{20.1 - 9.5} = 0.6321$$

$$S_{14} = \frac{15.7 - 8.7}{18.8 - 9.5} = 0.7527$$

$$S_{15} = \frac{16.2 - 8.7}{30.3 - 9.5} = 0.3606$$

$$S_{23} = \frac{15.4 - 9.5}{20.1 - 18.0} = 2.8095$$

$$S_{24} = \frac{15.7 - 9.5}{18.8 - 18.0} = 7.7500$$

$$S_{25} = \frac{16.2 - 9.5}{30.3 - 18.0} = 0.5447$$

$$S_{34} = \frac{15.7 - 15.4}{18.8 - 20.1} = -0.2308$$

$$S_{35} = \frac{16.2 - 15.4}{30.3 - 20.1} = 0.0784$$

$$S_{45} = \frac{16.2 - 15.7}{30.3 - 18.8} = 0.0435$$

Ordered array

-0.2308	0.5447
0.0435	0.6321
0.0784	0.7527
0.0941	2.8095
0.3606	7.7500

$$\hat{\beta} = \frac{0.3606 + 0.5447}{2} = 0.4526$$

$$S_{\alpha/2} = 10, \qquad C_{\alpha/2} = 10 - 2 = 8, \qquad k = \frac{10 - 8}{2} = 1$$

$$\hat{\beta}_L = -0.2308, \qquad \hat{\beta}_U = 7.7500$$

10.7

Ordered array of S_{ij}

-83.3333	23.7785
-79.3103	26.3780
-42.5926	37.9447
-0.5865	40.7547
1.0152	100.0000
7.9412	372.7273
11.0795	2900.0000
11.3208	

$\widehat{\beta} = 11.3208, \qquad S_{\alpha/2} = 13, \qquad C_{\alpha/2} = 13 - 2 = 11$

$k = \dfrac{15 - 11}{2} = 2, \qquad \widehat{\beta}_L = -79.3103, \qquad \widehat{\beta}_U = 372.7273$

10.8

Solution varies, depending on which values are randomly eliminated from the data set.

10.9

Solution varies, depending on which values are randomly eliminated from the data set.

10.10

Solution varies, depending on which values are randomly eliminated from the data set.

10.11

Solution varies, depending on which values are randomly eliminated from the data set.

10.12

Solution varies, depending on which values are randomly eliminated from the.data set.

10.13

Solution varies, depending on which values are randomly eliminated from the data set.

10.14

$S_{12} = -10.0000 \qquad S_{13} = 1.6667 \qquad S_{14} = -7.5000$

$S_{15} = 7.0000 \qquad S_{16} = 1.1111 \qquad S_{17} = 1.6667$

$S_{23} = -1.2500 \qquad S_{24} = -5.0000 \qquad S_{25} = -1.5000$

$S_{26} = 2.5000 \qquad S_{27} = 7.5000 \qquad S_{34} = -2.0000$

$S_{35} = -1.0000$ $S_{36} = 1.2500$ $S_{37} = 1.6667$

$S_{45} = -2.6667$ $S_{46} = 3.5714$ $S_{47} = 20.0000$

$S_{56} = 1.7000$ $S_{57} = 3.0000$ $S_{67} = 0.83333$

Ordered array of S_{ij}

-10.0000	-1.0000	1.7000
-7.5000	0.8333	2.5000
-5.0000	1.1111	3.0000
-2.6667	1.2500	3.5714
-2.0000	1.6667	7.0000
-1.5000	1.6667	7.5000
-1.2500	1.6667	20.0000

$S_{\alpha/2} = 15,$ $C_{\alpha/2} = 13,$ $k = \dfrac{21 - 13}{2} = 4$

$\widehat{\beta}_L = -2.6667,$ $\widehat{\beta}_U = 3.5714$

10.15

X	Y	Natural order	Reverse natural order
189	94	9	2
191	92	9	1
193	95	8	1
201	91	8	0
207	103	3	4
208	100	4	2
211	98	5	0
215	99	4	0
221	101	3	0
222	109	0	2
223	105	1	0
231	106	0	0

$P = 54,$ $Q = 12,$ $S = 54 - 12 = 42$

$\widehat{\tau} = \dfrac{42}{12(11)/2} = 0.6364,$ P value < 0.005

10.16

X	Y	Natural order	Reverse natural order
13	15	7	1
17	21	3	4
24	17	4	2
26	16	4	1
28	14	4	0
29	18	3	0
37	23	1	1
40	22	1	0
41	24	0	0
		27	9

$$\hat{\tau} = \frac{18}{9(8)/2} = 0.500 \qquad P \text{ value} = 0.05$$

10.17

Ordered array of S_{ij}

-1.0000	0.3125
-0.7500	0.3214
-0.6364	0.3333
-0.5556	0.3636
-0.5000	0.4118
-0.3333	0.4286
-0.0667	0.4615
-0.0159	0.5000
0.0435	0.5333
0.0769	0.5714
0.1000	0.6250
0.1250	0.6667
0.1818	0.6667
0.1875	0.7693
0.2000	1.0000
0.2500	1.5000
0.2500	2.0000
0.2593	4.0000

$$S_{\alpha/2} = 20, \qquad C_{\alpha/2} = 18, \qquad k = \frac{36 - 18}{2} = 9$$

$$\hat{\beta}_L = 0.0435, \qquad \hat{\beta}_U = 0.5714$$

10.18

Solution varies, depending on which values are randomly
eliminated from the data set.

ABCDEFGHIJ-A-798